PLANT BREEDING FOR EVERYONE

How to find and develop new plant varieties

JOHN Y. BEATY

A former associate of Luther Burbank

CHARLES T. BRANFORD COMPANY
BOSTON 16, MASSACHUSETTS

COPYRIGHT, 1954

JOHN Y. BEATY

First Printing

LIBRARY OF CONGRESS CATALOG CARD NUMBER: 53-7212

Printed in the United States of America

TABLE OF CONTENTS

I

You Can Find New Plant Varieties

A GARDEN CLUB MEMBER in Illinois found an ever-blooming delphinium in her garden. There was only one plant that bore blossoms, early, mid-season, and late. She mentioned it to me one day when I was talking before the garden club and I explained to her that this one plant was evidently a new variety—an everbearing delphinium. This plant was growing among others which bloomed only once during the season and it had certain blossom characteristics which made it more valuable than the others in this garden. It appeared also that these characteristics would make it desirable in any garden.

SEEDSMEN BUY NEW VARIETIES OF FLOWERS

An older woman who had been a flower enthusiast for many years was working in her bed of peonies one day when she noticed that the blossoms on one plant seemed to be quite different from those on the others. This surprised her because she had never given a thought to the possibility of a new variety showing up in her garden.

She examined the blossoms carefully. The petals were larger than those on other plants. The blossoms themselves were almost a third larger. The petals were compact. She picked one of the blossoms and took it into the house. It remained bright for many days.

The color was slightly different from the others in the bed. In fact, it was a color which is probably not found in any other peony variety. The following year, she took one of the blossoms to a nurseryman who specialized in peonies. He was enthusiastic about the flower at once. He went with her to her home and examined the plant. It was a large plant. It would be easy to divide the roots. He offered her $10.00 for the plant. This seemed like a good price to her and she sold the new variety, retaining the privilege of keeping enough of the root to have a plant of this kind in her garden the following year.

1

$50 A BULB FOR A NEW GLADIOLUS

A farmer in another state was going through his gladiolus bed one day when he noticed one spike which had blossoms growing all around it and so close together that the spike appeared almost like one blossom. He watched this plant and noted that the blossoms remained bright and thrifty for many days—much longer than the blossoms on other plants. The color was slightly different and there were streaks in the blossoms at such a place that they made the flower very distinctive and attractive. He took the spike to a gladiolus dealer about twenty miles away. The dealer was enthusiastic. He asked the farmer to bring in all available bulbs. The next day this farmer received what, to him, was a fabulous price—$50 a bulb.

A New York housewife had a somewhat similar experience. However, her gladiolus was quite different from the one the farmer sold at $50 a bulb. This lady eventually sold the bulbs from her new variety for $250 each!

NEW AMARYLLIS VARIETIES SELL FOR $2.00 TO $350

When I was working with Luther Burbank many years ago, he had 136 new varieties of amaryllis which he believed were ready to sell to seedsmen. He had 163 bulbs of one new variety, but only one bulb of another. He described each of these new varieties briefly in a printed pamphlet and mailed it to all the seedsmen in America.

Here is his description of No. 1: "Early. Extraordinary multiplier. Clear. Fiery scarlet. Broad petals. Much overlapping and recurved. Narrow white stripe at base of each petal. Four blossoms to each stalk. Sometimes three stalks to each bulb. Flowers average 8 inches across. Outer petals 3 inches wide. Average height 15 inches. 163 bulbs. Price $200.00."

No. 119 in the list was described as follows: "Fire crimson. Recurved lily-like petals, lightly lined with crimson and short bands of white. Height 2½ ft. 1 bulb, $2.00."

His highest priced collection of bulbs of one new variety he named "Martinique." He described it as follows:

"A remarkable new hybrid of the Sprekelia Formosissima or Jacobean lily with the Amaryllis (Hippeastrum) Vittata. One of the most unique hybrids which has been produced among the bulbous plants. The flowers are fiery crimson like those of the Jacobean lily but very much larger, being 9 inches in diameter, *but even* more remarkable are the long curious twisted petals which give the flowers a strange appearance, not found anywhere else among the Amaryllidae. Leaves pale green, upright, strap shape, 1 inch wide, 18 to 20 inches long. Flowers fiery crimson on slender stems 1½ to 2 feet long. Usually two flowers to each stem. I have now produced 58 large bulbs and 57 small ones of this new hybrid. Price for the whole stock without reserve, $350."

While the 136 varieties described in this pamphlet were priced at a total of $4,841, it must be realized, of course, that this collection of new flowers was not developed in one year. It is difficult to say how much work had been spent on the hybridizing and selection of these new varieties.

This information discloses the fact that money is paid for new varieties of flowers—sometimes a small amount, sometimes quite a large amount.

In addition to buying new varieties outright, it occasionally happens that a nurseryman or seedsman will pay a royalty on the quantity he sells. Each year, he determines how many of the new variety have been sold and pays the originator an agreed-upon amount for each one sold. As an illustration, a new variety of rose sold on a royalty basis resulted in royalties of $1,587 in 3 years after the rose was first listed in the nurseryman's catalogue.

NEW FRUIT VARIETIES SOMETIMES BRING HIGH PRICES

A 75-year-old man in Colorado found growing in his orchard an apricot tree which had come from seed. He showed it to a nurseryman and it proved to be such a valuable new variety that the nurseryman paid him $2,500 for the right to introduce it.

A. H. Mullins, a farmer of West Virginia whose farm was "way back in the hills," received $5,000 for a tree which grew from seed. It was the original Golden Delicious apple tree.

$6,000 FOR THE BRANCH OF AN APPLE TREE

Lewis Mood of New Jersey found one branch on a Delicious apple tree which had bright red apples when the other apples on the tree were still green. So attractive was this new variety of Delicious apple that Stark Bros. Nursery Co. of Louisiana, Missouri, paid him $6,000 for the branch on which these red apples grew. It was introduced as the "Starking Delicious."

The Wilson blackberry which has made millions of dollars for growers was found in the garden of an amateur.

The St. Regis raspberry was found growing wild on a farm in Hammonton, New Jersey.

Elmer Gove of Burlington, Vermont, listed 50 new varieties of gladiolus in his 1951 catalogue. At least 19 of these were seedlings. That is, the new variety grew as a result of someone's merely planting a gladiolus seed. It was as easy as that!

As you can see from the examples given, it may be profitable to discover useful new varieties. Nurserymen and seedsmen are on the lookout for new varieties to introduce each year.

A NEW PLANT VARIETY IS A CONTRIBUTION TO MANKIND

There's money in discovering new varieties as well as pleasure and satisfaction. When you provide a new plant variety for mankind, you are accomplishing far more than most people realize. You are benefiting the lives of thousands—probably millions of people, some still unborn. A new variety that proves to be worthy may continue to serve mankind for years—possibly for generations.

THERE MAY BE A NEW VARIETY IN YOUR GARDEN NOW!

It is possible that an important new variety of plant may now be growing in your own garden. To introduce it may be as great a contribution to the welfare of mankind as the invention of a new chemical or a new machine. Many new varieties of flowers, fruits, and vegetables have been found by gardeners and fruit growers.

It is not difficult to learn how to recognize a new variety, to evaluate its characters, to propagate and test it, and to introduce it through a seedsman or nurseryman. Each of these steps is clearly explained in this book.

EVERY FRUIT SEED PRODUCES SOMETHING DIFFERENT

Seeds from most plants which are propagated by vegetative methods; such as, budding, grafting, layering, cuttings, tubers, bulbs, etc., practically never produce seedlings which are identical with the parent variety. Such is the case with plants like the apple, plum, grape, strawberry, potato, gladiolus, tulip, dahlia, peony, and a whole list of herbaceous perennials as well as some shrubs.

The reason for this situation is twofold: (1) with plants which are to be vegetatively reproduced, it is not necessary to "purify" a new variety in order for it to remain true to type when multiplied for distribution; (2) most plants of this type are subject to cross-pollination in nature and therefore each seed is likely to produce a plant somewhat different from either parent.

Not all of these new seedlings will be as good as those plants on which the seeds grew. Most of them, in fact, will be inferior—quite useless; but now and then, one will be more useful than the varieties now available. There may be a dahlia with an entirely new color. A gladiolus may have a flower stem bearing three or four times as many blossoms. An apple seedling may produce a new variety of fruit as valuable as the Golden Delicious. A grape seedling may produce a new variety of grape with larger berries, larger bunches, and a more delicious flavor than the parent variety.

The seeds of some of our plants which are commonly propagated by seeds may also grow into a new variety, although that is not so common. The point is, *be on the look-out for plants in your garden which show new and desirable characteristics.*

Seedlings, however, are not our only source of new varieties of plants. "Sports," or "mutants," occur quite often. The Starking Delicious apple was what is commonly known as a "bud sport." One bud on a Delicious tree grew into a branch which produced the new variety.

NEW VARIETIES MAY BE FOUND IN THE WOODS OR FIELDS

You may discover a new variety in the woods, fields, or in an orchard. It may be either a seedling or a mutant. If the entire plant or tree is a new variety, it is a *seedling*. If only one portion of the plant or tree is different, it probably is a *bud sport* or *mutant*. If you travel to other countries, you may discover a variety there which might well be introduced into the United States.

A WILD TREE BECOMES USEFUL

As an example of a discovery in the woods, here's the story of Hiram H. Owens of Barbourville, Kentucky. Mr. Owens once wrote: "Nine years ago, I was driving south of Barbourville and noticed two small dogwood trees growing together in a clay bank. I took them home and planted them in my yard. One of them died, but the other one lived and when it came to bloom, it had blossoms of tremendous size. I sent two of the blossoms to Stark Bros. of Louisiana, Missouri, and they wired me that they were interested in the new variety which apparently was a wild seedling.

"The blossoms of the new dogwood tree are about five inches across and are a beautiful pink color."

ONE SEEDLING CREATED A $17,000,000 INDUSTRY

Over 100 years ago on a Massachusetts farm, a boy found a seed ball on an Early Rose potato plant. When the seed ball was ripe, it was picked and there proved to be 23 seeds inside. These seeds were planted the next year and 23 new seedling potatoes were produced. Only two of them, however, were worthy of consideration. One of those was sold to a seedsman and, today, that variety which was started by a small boy is the basis for an industry in our northwestern states which amounts to about seventeen million dollars' worth of potatoes per year.

The boy's name was Luther Burbank. The potato was originally named "Burbank's Seedling." In Chicago, it is now referred to as the "Idaho" potato. It may have other names, but it illustrates emphatically the importance of watching for new varieties and making an effort to bring them about. It illustrates how tremendously important one new variety may become.

Hand Pollination Yields New Varieties

Roderick W. Cumming, a seedsman, tells me of an experiment with the bush honeysuckle which proved most valuable. Here's the way he explained his experience in a letter:

"Probably the best and quickest results I ever obtained from hand pollination resulted from the crossing of Weigela Eva Rathke and Weigela Rosea. This was done on one branch of Rosea and took but a matter of moments and yet gave about 200 seedlings the following spring. These were lined out for two years until flowering, at which time they were cut down to ten. Out of this ten, one was selected and named Weigela Bristol Ruby. The whole process took very little labor and presented us with a new hybrid very easy to handle and propagate, and one which has proved quite profitable."

This is an illustration of the results which may be obtained by cross pollinating plants of different varieties. More detailed information on cross pollination and the production of hybrids will be given in Chapters XIV, XV, and XVI.

A White Chrysanthemum Produced Some Yellow Blossoms

Mr. Cumming tells of another experience, which illustrates how a sport may be discovered among flowers in any garden. This was with a chrysanthemum variety. His description of the experience referred to is as follows:

"Another new plant from a different source has come to us in the new pompon chrysanthemum, Canary Wonder. This should be more or less of a world beater because it brings in an entirely new color for its class; namely, a soft canary-primrose yellow.

"In the Fall of 1949, one plant of the pompon, White Wonder, sported over one-half of its vegetative area to this new shade of yellow. We were very lucky to get thirteen of the hard wood bud divisions of the stems to take root and, as they put out new tops during the winter, we snatched every available cutting. By continuing this until early June, we were able to get about 165 nice plants. This will serve as an example of luck and may remind your readers of the necessity of keeping their eyes open, for *sports may be found in any garden.*"

A Seedling Dianthus Became a Popular Variety

The importance and the value of being alert to new varieties and their characteristics is illustrated still further by Mr. Cumming in the following case:

"Still another case of someone keeping his eyes open is shown in our hardy Dianthus, Wallace Red. We are a little vague on its origin ourselves but understand that a perennial grower saw it in a batch of seedlings in Buffalo, New York, and noticed it at once, although it was badly crowded and suffering from lack of care. Unable to make cuttings, he divided the plant for several years and had worked up a stock of about 50. We saw it three Falls ago, secured a couple of plants from him and have since managed to sell several thousand of them. Here is an example of a case in which a good plant might well have passed unnoticed if our friend had not been on the alert for such improvements."

To sum up—new varieties may be discovered in your own garden, in the woods or fields, in other parts of the country, or in fact in foreign countries. These new varieties may be seedlings or mutants, or hybrids produced by man. As Mr. Cumming says, it is important to be alert to new varieties and to make them available through nurserymen and seedsmen when you discover one that seems to you to be useful.

EVERY PLANT IS DIFFERENT IN SOME WAY

The basis for new varieties, both from seed and from sports, is this principle: *there are no two things in this world exactly alike.* In a bed of flowers which at first glance appears to be uniform, you may find a single plant which has blossoms of a different color, shape or size. It may be something worthy of introduction.

Quite commonly, however, those plants which we reproduce by seed are said to be "uniform." What we mean is that they are sufficiently alike so that we can depend upon the qualities to expect when we plant the seed. That doesn't mean that every plant, or every blossom, is exactly the same.

HYBRIDS OCCUR AMONG WILD PLANTS

In addition to getting new varieties from seedlings, some of which may be of value, we can cross-pollinate the flowers of different plants with the hope that the resulting hybrid may be quite different from either one. In many cases, the bees do this hybridizing work for us. The hummingbird may have a part in it. Even the wind carries pollen from one plant to another in some species.

It is easy to understand that hybrids are being made all the time in nature. That is why we sometimes discover a valuable new variety in the woods or fields when we had nothing to do with its development.

After having visited with many people who have discovered or brought about new varieties by hybridization, I am sure that *the discovery and introduction of a new variety of plant is one of life's greatest opportunities.*

II

How to Recognize a New Variety

I THINK Luther Burbank stimulated interest in the search for new varieties as much as any other one man. I had the rare privilege of working with him many years ago and he often emphasized the fact that new varieties are coming into existence constantly—thousands of them—yes, millions. However, thousands and even millions of seedlings are of little value because most of them are inferior to varieties now available. Still, one in a million, one in a thousand, or (in some cases) one in a hundred, may have special merit. The point is, we should all be on the look-out for desirable new plants so that none will die without being appropriated for the use of mankind.

A Valuable New Apple Was Lost

At one time, A. C. Campbell of Chelan, Washington, discovered some unusual apples in a basket brought in by one of his pickers. Without a doubt, the apples had grown as a bud sport on one of his orchard trees, for there were no young trees just coming into bearing.

He showed samples of the apples to a nurseryman who was struck by their beauty and usefulness and offered to buy the branch on which the apples grew. Unfortunately, the pickers could not tell Mr. Campbell from which tree the apples were gathered. The new variety was lost temporarily.

Without a doubt, there have been thousands of new varieties lost in just this way. Many garden club members may have looked directly at new flowers in their gardens and not realized that they might be of unusual value. The purpose of this book is to encourage everyone who reads it to realize that new varieties are worth money because they may add to the pleasure and usefulness of millions of people if they are introduced.

Study the Characters of Present Varieties

The way to recognize a new variety is to study the characters of present varieties. Unless you are familiar

Stark Bro's Nurseries

4. THIS GOLDEN DELICIOUS APPLE TREE, PRODUCED BY GRAFT-
ING SMALL CION FROM ORIGINAL TREE IN W. VIRGINIA ONTO A ROOT STOCK.
WHEN 3 FEET HIGH, GRAFTED TREE TRANSPLANTED TO ORCHARD OF CLAUDE
SHINN, NEW HARTFORD, ILLINOIS. PICTURE SHOWS TREE, A HEAVY BEARER,
4 YEARS OLD

3. THE FAMOUS STARKING TREE IN THE CAGE

6. McGREDY'S SUNSET (PLANT PATENT 317) IS A YELLOW ROSE
WITH FRAGRANT FLOWERS OF CLEAR SUNSHINY YELLOW PENCILLED WITH
CARMINE

5. WORLD'S FAIR. LARGE, SEMI-DOUBLE, DEEP CRIMSON FLOWERS FADE TO SCARLET

with what is already being sold, you may not realize that you are looking at something worthwhile, even though it appears to be different from others in your own garden.

This principle suggests that it might be well to specialize in one type of flower, or one type of fruit, and become an expert, for example, on the subject of daisies, gladioli, or lilies, so that your familiarity with the varieties now being grown will enable you quickly to recognize characters which may make a new discovery more useful than plants we already have.

A beginning toward developing your knowledge of different types of plants may be made by obtaining various nursery and seed catalogues. In them, you will learn about the varieties available. Many of them contain colored pictures. The cost of this beginning will be very little, for most seedsmen and nurserymen are willing to send their catalogues free.

The next step would be to purchase seeds or plants of the kind which interests you most and grow them in your own garden. This will increase your knowledge of the characters which have seemed desirable to those who introduced the varieties you are growing.

There are also many books available in which you can learn about the many plants now being grown.

Make Lists of Plant Characteristics

As you study your chosen plant or plants, it would be very wise to make a list of the desirable characteristics which you find in each variety. It would be worth while also to make a list of undesirable characteristics any one or more of which might make a new variety worthless. The experience gained in making these two lists will be of great value when you look through your garden hoping to find something new. It will help develop your ability to recognize a desirable new plant.

Hardiness Is of First Importance

Without a doubt, hardiness is an important characteristic in any plant. If a plant is injured by cold, heat, excessive rainfall, or any other vicissitude, its good characteristics may be worthless because it will be difficult to grow that plant successfully. There are, of course, degrees of hardiness as well as different types of hardiness.

Perhaps the second most important characteristic is vigor. A vigorous plant is easy to raise. One that grows slowly may have to be discarded for that undesirable characteristic alone.

DISEASE- AND PEST-RESISTANT VARIETIES ARE GREATLY NEEDED

Probably one of the greatest needs among gardeners today is new varieties of each type of plant which will be resistant to pests and diseases. Quite a number of new varieties of gladioli, tomatoes, and other plants have already been discovered which appear to resist those pests and diseases which have become serious, especially in commercial planting.

If you are going through your vegetable garden some day and note that an insect, a nematode worm, or a disease is destroying some of your tomato plants, examine every plant carefully to see if there might be one which is not harmed. That one may be a new form resistant to the pest.

Save the seeds from the tomatoes growing on that plant and test them the following year. Give a few to your friends to test, and note results. If the results are plants which resist disease or insects or worms, you may have a new variety valuable entirely because of its resistance.

Just think of the amount of work now required for spraying and other means of combating disease and insects which can be saved by resistant varieties! Even though the fruit of such a plant were not quite so good as some others, it might be in great demand entirely because of its resistance.

THERE IS A DESIRABLE SIZE FOR EACH FRUIT

Another important characteristic is the *size of the plant, the flower, the fruit, or the root, depending upon which part of the plant is most used.* Large size usually is of special value, although there may be cases in which a flower or fruit can be too large, or the roots—if the roots are used—can be too large. There is a desirable size. You may discover a new variety which provides that desirable characteristic.

Certainly, *prolificacy* is a characteristic which is highly desirable, especially in commercial planting. You may discover a single plant which has a much more profitable yield of the useful part than any others now grown. That alone might justify its introduction.

The *quality* of the useful part may increase or decrease demand for the variety. What we refer to as "improved quality" is a difficult thing to define accurately, for it all depends on the use to be made of the plant and the demand among those people who buy it.

Sometimes, a new plant is discovered which suggests *a use not now made of that type of plant.* The new plant may have greater food value before or after cooking. It may make excellent preserves or jelly, or have special qualities for quick freezing, canning, or shipping, or have greater value for livestock feed.

ADAPTABILITY TO CLIMATE AND SOIL IS IMPORTANT

Unless a new variety is adapted to the climate or common soil conditions, it may be of no value. On the other hand, if you find a variety which has *wide adaptability*— which can be grown either in Minnesota or Florida, Massachusetts or California—the very fact that it is adapted to the different types of climate may be the reason why it is more valuable than varieties we now have.

You may discover a variety which is especially thrifty when grown in a greenhouse, or in hot beds. *Adaptability to various growing conditions is an important characteristic.*

TIME OF RIPENING MAY MAKE A NEW VARIETY SALEABLE

You may find a new variety which matures its blossoms or ripens its fruits or its other edible parts at a different season from the varieties now being used. That might make the new variety especially desirable. Or you might discover one which is everblooming or everbearing—one which bears through the entire growing season. This has been the reason for the introduction of many new varieties of flowers and several strawberries, for example.

Perhaps the easiest characteristic to recognize is that of *color*. A gladiolus with a new color of blossoms may be worthy of introduction for that characteristic alone. Some other plant with a foliage of a different shade may be of value for that change of color. Many new varieties of fruits have been introduced entirely for the reason that they provided a more attractive or a greater amount of color. The Starking Delicious apple, for example, was introduced for that reason. Other Delicious apples were less well colored. There are many color variations being produced in amateur gardens every year. *Watch for a color change!*

You might find one strawberry plant which was producing a strawberry of *a different shape*. That characteristic might be sufficient to justify introduction of the new variety. A new shape of daisy, a new shape of apple, a new shape of the plant itself, or of its root if the root is used for food, might represent a desirable characteristic.

You Can Plan a New Variety—and Get It

Let me emphasize again that, with the help of the list given in this chapter, you should make out a list of *desirable* characteristics and *undesirable* characteristics for each type of plant which interests you. Then, make a careful study of varieties now available and note the characteristics which each of these varieties already has provided for our use. Perhaps this study will prompt you to determine what desirable characteristics are needed and then you will have something definite to look for and to work toward.

It is entirely possible to plan a new variety theoretically and then work toward the characteristics you have set up. Just how that is done will be explained in Chapter XII.

Following is a list of some of the desirable characters in plants. Another list shows inferior characters. You may think of still others.

SUPERIOR CHARACTERS

HARDINESS

1 Hardy in a cold climate
2 Hardy in a hot climate
3 Hardy in a wet climate
4 Hardy in a dry climate
5 Drought resistant
6 Improved adaptability to local conditions
7 Resistant to cracking
8 Resistant to disease
9 Resistant to pests

YIELD

10 Heavy yielder
11 Large edible parts
12 Sets fruit under adverse conditions
13 Ripens evenly
14 Easily harvested
15 Waste parts have feeding value
16 All plant parts useful

MARKETABILITY

17 Early maturity
18 Late season maturity
19 Mid-season maturity
20 Everbearing
21 Uniformity
22 Attractive appearance
23 New and attractive color
24 Adapted to cold storage
25 Adapted to quick freezing
26 Suitable for canning
27 Little waste
28 New and desirable flavor
29 New and desirable odor
30 Smooth fruit
31 Seedless
32 Small seeds
33 Thin rind
34 Good shipping quality
35 Popular or desirable shape
36 Keeps well in home storage
37 Solid flesh
38 Juicy
39 Convenient size
40 High sugar content
41 Novelty
42 Special character such as popping quality in popcorn
43 Suitable for jellies and preserves

PLANT QUALITIES

44 Vigorous grower
45 Uniformity
46 Thornlessness
47 Resistant to sun scald
48 Good pollen producer for hybridization

INFERIOR CHARACTERS

LACK OF HARDINESS

1 Injured by cold weather
2 Injured by hot weather
3 Injured by excess rain
4 Injured by dry weather
5 Cannot withstand drought
6 Not adapted to local conditions
7 Fruit cracks in ripening
8 Succumbs to prevalent diseases
9 Succumbs to prevalent pests

UNSATISFACTORY YIELD

10 Small yield
11 Small edible parts
12 Doesn't always set fruit
13 Ripens unevenly
14 Difficult to harvest
15 Waste parts worthless
16 Only one part useful

MARKETABILITY

17 Uneven maturity
18 Matures when demand is light
19 Matures when competition is greatest
20 No uniformity in edible parts

21 Unattractive appearance
22 Undesirable color
23 Not suitable for cold storage
24 Not suitable for quick freezing
25 Not suitable for canning
26 Too much waste
27 Undesirable flavor
28 Flavor not new
29 Undesirable odor
30 Rough skin
31 Warty skin
32 Too many seeds

33 Seeds too large
34 Thick rind
35 Poor shipper
36 Undesirable shape
37 Flesh soft
38 Poor keeper in home storage
39 Little juice
40 Undesirable size
41 Low sugar content
42 Novelty, but not popular
43 No desirable special characters
44 Not suitable for jellies or preserves

PLANT QUALITIES

45 Weak grower
46 Little uniformity
47 Thorny

48 Wood subject to sun scald
49 Poor pollen producer
50 Sterile

III

New Varieties May Be Obtained by Selection Only

IF YOU visualize a daisy which might be desirable, you may be able to develop it by selecting those plants in your bed of daisies which are nearest to the type desired.

Let us say, for example, that you wanted a variety with longer petals. By carefully studying and measuring the length of the petals, you would find one or more plants which had petals longer than the others. By planting seeds from those, the next year you would be likely to find other plants whose petals were even longer than the parents. By keeping this up generation after generation, you would stand a good chance of developing the type of daisy you wanted sooner or later.

A VALUABLE NEW VARIETY OF CANNING PEAS WAS DEVELOPED BY SELECTION

There is variation in the plants in every bed of flowers or in every bed of vegetables. For example, at one time a canner of garden peas in Colorado wanted a variety which could be harvested by machinery so that the individual pods would not need to be picked by hand. He also wanted a variety whose peas were comparatively small in the pod and comparatively uniform. Obviously, the variety must be such that the pods would all be ready to harvest at about the same time.

The president of the company wrote a letter to Luther Burbank at Santa Rosa, California, and asked him if he could produce such a variety. Mr. Burbank told me of his methods of selecting individual plants which eventually resulted in a new variety of peas having the specifications given by the canner. He explained his experience as follows:

"I selected in successive generations those vines which came nearest to meeting the specifications as to number of pods, uniformity of ripening, and a uniformly small

17

size of the peas in the pods. I watched the individual plants in order that I might select only the very best from the standpoint of vigor and hardiness. I counted the pods and counted the peas in the pod from each selection and made a careful record of those seeds which I saved. I destroyed the other plants in the bed which were not developing in the direction desired.

"I was able to grow two crops each year and thus speeded up the work. In three years (that is, six generations) by selection alone, I was able to have a new variety which met all of the specifications of the canner."

That was in 1911. In 1946, the writer, giving a talk to the Rotary Club in Denver, Colorado, asked the chairman if, by any chance, Mr. Empson of the Empson Canning Co. was present.

"Yes," he said. "He sits right there in the front row."

I stepped down and asked Mr. Empson about the variety of peas which Mr. Burbank had developed for him.

"We are still using it," he said. "It is our best variety, and we have used it all these years. It comes true to form every year."

That is an outstanding example of visualizing a new variety and eventually developing it by merely selecting those individual plants which come nearest to the desired quality.

FARM CROPS ARE IMPROVED BY SELECTION

Several new varieties of oats have been announced in recent years which have been produced by one of the workers at the Iowa State College at Ames, Iowa, by selection alone. In other words, only those oat plants were selected which had the characteristics desired. Their seeds were planted and again only the most desirable plants were saved; the seeds replanted, and so on.

In recent years, the corn borer has caused considerable damage in the corn-growing states. Several experiment stations have worked toward varieties which are resistant to that pest, and at the time this is written, a number of new varieties have been introduced which are quite resistant.

This work, however, has not been done by selection alone, but rather by *hybridization* followed by selection. Hybridization is a matter of controlling the pollen which fertilizes the silk on certain selected stalks. The choice of those stalks which are used for this hybridization, however, is entirely a matter of selection. By going through field after field, the workers discover an occasional stalk, or several stalks, which seem not to be injured by the corn borer. These are marked, and when the ears are mature, the kernels from those ears are used to plant new crops from which pollen will be taken to fertilize other selected plants.

A tomato variety known as Indian Baltimore became an important canning variety. It was developed by selection alone.

Selection may continue over several years depending upon what characters are desired and how long it takes to perfect them.

Many Peppers and Muskmelons Were Developed by Selection

The Year Book of the United States Department of Agriculture for 1939 states: "Practically all of the large-fruited mild-fleshed varieties of peppers were developed by selection. A single pepper plant selected by S. D. Riegel of Georgia and named Perfection had all of the qualities needed. It was selected from a bed grown from imported seed.

"All our important commercial varieties of eggplant are the result of work by private gardeners and seedsmen and mostly by selection."

A green-fleshed muskmelon was selected from a field of Rocky Ford and named Pollock. It proved to be a valuable variety. In another case, a fruit bearing a salmon tint flesh was selected and was introduced as Salmon Tint.

The Hale Best is another variety of muskmelon developed entirely by selection from the seeds obtained from a Japanese gardener in the Imperial Valley of California.

It was introduced in 1924 and became the leading commercial and shipping variety because it matured early in the season.

Many Cabbage and Bean Varieties Were Developed by Selection

The following varieties of cabbage which may be familiar to you were all developed by selection:

1	Burpee's All Head Early	7	Mason
2	Large Wakefield	8	Stone Mason
3	Ferry's Hollander	9	Ferry's Round Dutch
4	Fattler's Drumhead	10	Gill's Oregon Baldhead
5	Hawser	11	Mid-Season Market
6	Succession	12	Early Danish

Varieties of beans which were developed entirely by selection will be found listed in various seed catalogues as follows: Fordhook, Great Northern, Baby Potato Lima, Robust, Waltham's Scarlet.

Other varieties of vegetables produced by selection only are: California Canner's Spinach, Maryland Alaska Peas, Illinois Pride Tomatoes.

You May Select New Fruit Varieties

Occasionally, trees develop from the seeds of fruits which drop in the orchard or elsewhere. These seedlings most often bear fruit (if they are left to fruiting age) that is of less value than the tree on which the seeds grew. However, sometimes there is a seedling which has desirable fruit.

A neighbor of mine found a seedling like this in his apple orchard. For the past several years he has been harvesting and using the big apples which grow on that seedling tree. He didn't realize that there might be some value in offering this new apple to a nurseryman.

At my suggestion, he sent it to a nurseryman. The dealer reported that the apple is a desirable variety but it happens that this nurseryman has another variety so near like it that he did not wish to buy it. My friend, however, will send samples of the fruit to other nurserymen and, undoubtedly, he will find one who will introduce it. It will then be not only of money value to him, but also of value to all those who benefit from its use in the years to come.

SELECTIONS MAY BE MADE FROM WILD PLANTS

It is probably safe to say that wild plants offer just as good a source of new varieties as cultivated ones. All of our cultivated plants were once wild. As a matter of fact, there are many beautiful flowers in the woods and fields which might well be planted in our gardens, particularly if we select individuals. Certainly, the Black-Eyed Susan and the cone flowers would be considered beautiful additions to our gardens but, for some reason or other, little attention has been given to them. They are still called "weeds."

If you were to examine carefully the blossoms of every Black-Eyed Susan you find, you probably would be able to select some which have larger blossoms and more attractive stems and leaves than others. The seeds from these could be saved and planted in your garden. Then, from the resulting plants, you could make further selections until you finally would have a superior seedling which you would be entitled to name—a variety which would be acceptable to other gardeners.

SOME WEEDS CAN BE MADE USEFUL

Someone has defined a weed as "a plant out of place." I should like to suggest another definition: "A weed is a plant we have not yet learned how to use." I feel sure that many of those plants which we now call "weeds" might be selected and cultivated to the extent that they eventually would become useful plants.

The outstanding characteristics of most weeds are *vigor* and *hardiness*. Those are two characteristics very much desired in cultivated plants. The job is to select those weeds which have parts which we can use and individuals which have developed those parts to a more desirable degree than others have done.

Careful selection might result in a new type of wild rose which would be suitable for domestic use. The wild carrot, or Queen Anne's Lace, might easily be selected for large and beautiful blossoms. I have seen individual blossoms that were worthy of domestication.

The way to obtain an improvement over the wild type is to select seeds from those blossoms which are most attractive. Plant them in the garden and then make selections of the best blossoms resulting from that generation. Plant the seeds from those and continue selection year after year until you have blossoms which gardeners would like to grow both for outdoor decoration and for cut flowers.

The bushy aster and some of the other wild asters, the wild sunflower, the Jerusalem artichoke, the ox-eye daisy, and many, many more might be studied carefully and selections made with the result that new flower varieties might be made available to all gardeners.

THISTLES AND DANDELIONS MIGHT REWARD ATTENTION

It is entirely possible that even as undesirable a weed as the thistle might be selected for its flowers and foliage and for the lack of spines until a spineless, attractive plant resulted. I have seen wild thistles with white blossoms and white stems which were really beautiful.

Even our despised dandelion might be selected for size of blossom and prolific blooming tendencies, until we would have a border plant which we would enjoy. Perhaps control methods would need to be used to prevent the seeds from the domesticated dandelion from spreading to our lawns where it would become a pest as the wild dandelion now is a pest.

Don't despise the weed!

IV

How to Evaluate a New Variety

YOU MUST BE the first to evaluate the new variety of plant you find or develop. Later, you may get the opinion of a seedsman or nurseryman in order to make it available to all gardeners.

The first step is to make two lists. One will include those characters which make the plant useful at present. The other will be potential uses—new uses which might be made of the plant if a certain characteristic were developed. Each of these lists would probably contain one or more of the following:

COLOR	Edible Leaves	Edible Seeds	Suitable for cooking	A good keeper in storage
SIZE	Edible Stem	Edible Roots	Suitable for quick freezing	
FOLIAGE	Edible Tubers	Edible Fruits	Suitable for canning	Suitable for drying

You may think of other characters which would make the plant useful and, if you do, those should be listed, and each characteristic in the plant you are studying should then be evaluated. This evaluation might indicate that the character is as good as we now have, not as good as we now have, or better than we now have.

After you have evaluated the plant in this way, you will then be able to see from the list you have put on paper what characters are likely to make the new variety most valuable. You should then study the degree of development of each character in order to determine what additional work needs to be done.

Let us say, for example, that the plant with which you are working appears to be valuable because of certain qualities of its blossom. However, perhaps the size of that blossom is smaller than you desire. You want a larger flower. The usual way of attempting to obtain the result is to select the seeds from those individual plants which have blossoms larger than those on other plants. Plant them, and from the new plants resulting select those which bear the largest blossoms.

Sometimes it is possible to get what you want in one generation. At other times it may be necessary to grow several generations, planting seeds each year from selected individuals. In most parts of the United States we can grow only one generation of plants in a year. In some places like Florida, Texas, and California, it is possible to grow two or even three. *A generation in a plant is the period from seed to the production of new seed.*

GET YOUR FRIENDS TO GROW YOUR NEW VARIETY

A word of caution is necessary in order to encourage you to be patient until you have something that is really worthy. It is very easy to become enthusiastic over a new variety you discover or develop and your enthusiasm may cause you to overlook some undesirable character which someone else might see. For that reason, it is wise to ask your friends to evaluate what seems to you to be a good new plant, or a plant which is developing toward usefulness.

Then, when you finally have a variety which you think is ready for introduction, it is wise to give some of the seeds to a number of friends. Ask them to grow plants under different conditions in order to evaluate the new variety. They may disclose something good which you did not notice. Or they may disclose something undesirable which you had not seen.

TEST YOUR NEW VARIETY IN DIFFERENT CLIMATES

Inasmuch as lack of hardiness is the one character which may outshine all the good characters, it is wise to test a new variety under as many different climatic conditions as possible. For that reason, it is always helpful to send plants or seeds to friends in other climates. Have the seeds grown in a colder climate, in a hotter climate, in a drier climate, in a wetter climate, than your own.

If you know of a disease or pest in some other territory which is damaging the type of plant you are developing, it would certainly be wise to send plants or seeds there to be tested in the hope that your new plant might be resistant to the disease or pest.

LIST THE GOOD POINTS OF YOUR NEW VARIETY

After you think you have a new variety which is worthy, the next task is to grow it in a plot with existing varieties and list all of its advantages over them. This testing may be the best evidence you will have of the worthiness of the new plant. Records of this testing may be the means of your selling your new variety to a seedsman or nurseryman.

V

How to Evaluate Specific Characters

EACH IMPORTANT CHARACTER in a new plant needs to be compared with the same character in existing varieties. If, for example, you have a new gladiolus which you think is worthy because of the color of its blossoms, you would need to compare that color with other colors available. It might be that you would discover that there is already a good variety of approximately the same color.

That might not, however, be reason for destroying your plant, for it might have some other character which is more desirable than the variety of the same color which is already in existence. For example, the flower stem might be much longer. Perhaps the blossoms open all at once, or are of a different size. Sometimes smaller blossoms make an attractive garden flower, and that one character alone might make it worthy of introduction.

Each Individual Character Needs
Separate Consideration

The emphasis in this chapter is on the proposition that each individual character must be carefully evaluated in the light of your knowledge of other varieties of the same plant already in existence. That does not mean that every character must be different or better. *Color* alone may be the reason for introduction. *Vigor* or *disease resistance* may each in itself justify introduction.

With so many gladiolus varieties available, you might be discouraged because the task of comparison might appear to be too large. However, it is not difficult to get help in evaluating each specific character. There may be a gladiolus grower who has many varieties which he grows for the market who would be willing to give you his judgment as to the value of specific characters. There are wholesale seedsmen who specialize in growing gladioli for retailers. Inasmuch as their business is confined to this one type of plant, they know almost at a glance whether each character in your new variety is better or inferior to what already exists. Because of their interest in introducing new varieties, they can be depended upon to give their judgment whenever you ask it.

These specialists have test plots in which they test new varieties and it undoubtedly would be wise to send one or more of your bulbs for testing. Before you do this, of course, you should have worked with your new plant long enough so that you have a supply of a dozen bulbs or more.

DESIRABLE CHARACTERS IN GLADIOLI

One gladiolus specialist lists the following as desirable characters in this beautiful flower: tallest, earliest, largest, most open bloom, largest flower head, most beautiful, most unusual and striking, most heavily ruffled.

If your new variety is taller than others, you would be encouraged to send it to the gladiolus specialist just mentioned for testing because he lists in his catalogue 35 varieties under the heading of "tallest." He lists 22 varieties as "earliest." Your variety might be even earlier. He lists 21 varieties as "largest," and 22 as having the "largest flower heads." The name of this gladiolus specialist is Elmer Gove. He is the proprietor of Champlain View Gardens, Burlington, Vermont. If you are interested in the gladiolus, by all means get the catalogue issued by Champlain View Gardens, as well as the catalogues of every other gladiolus specialist.

MORE KINDS OF HOUSE PLANTS ARE NEEDED

If you are primarily interested in house plants, it may be that you could develop varieties of plants not commonly grown in the house which would be suitable for that use. It certainly is worth trying. In this case, you would evaluate the character which adapts the plant to growth in a small amount of soil and under the conditions existing in most homes. By transplanting several varieties of garden plants into flower pots or boxes and growing them in the house, you will discover that some are better adapted to such treatment than others.

LIST THE CHARACTERS NEEDED FOR EACH USE

In evaluating a specific character, it certainly is wise to list all of the variations of that character which you know about or which might occur. Then, indicate by check marks those which are most desirable and those which are least desirable.

Then make new lists, one list showing the degree of desirability of each character to be studied, the other list showing the various degrees of undesirability. The point is, we cannot expect perfection, but we do want to get each character developed to the highest point practicable. In this way, you will set up standards which you will consider the minimum for each character you are studying. Unless a plant comes up to or exceeds the minimum standard, you should either discard it or continue your work with it until it reaches or goes above the minimum standard.

Let us say, for example, that you have a tomato which you believe is resistant to Fusarium wilt. Some of the seedlings from that plant may be expected to show more or less resistance. You should note, from the time the tiny plants appear above the ground until they are mature, just what degree of resistance each plant exhibits. If there are some that seem to be perfect, they are the ones to keep for further work and for propagation.

After you have what you think is a thoroughly resistant tomato variety, you must, of course, then consider the other characters. If the fruit is of little value, the resistance alone may not justify introduction of the new kind. So you need to consider the individual characters of the fruit—size, color, flavor, time of ripening, and so on. Here's a list of some characters, each one of which needs to be evaluated separately:

EVALUATE EACH OF THESE CHARACTERS SEPARATELY

1 ADAPTED TO CLIMATIC CONDITIONS
2 ADAPTED TO SOIL CONDITIONS
3 DISEASE RESISTANCE
4 PEST RESISTANCE
5 SEASON: EARLY; MID; LATE
6 FLAVOR: SWEET; SOUR; SPECIAL
7 SIZE: PLANT; FRUIT; BLOSSOM
8 COLOR
9 SHAPE
10 CANNING SUITABILITY
11 SHIPPING QUALITIES
12 BLOSSOMS: LARGE; PERSISTENT; SHAPE; COLOR—PINK, RED, YELLOW, BLUE, BROWN, WHITE, VARIEGATED; FRAGRANCE
13 FOLIAGE: DEEP GREEN; LIGHT GREEN; VARIEGATED; RED; WHITE
14 PROLIFICACY OR YIELD
15 THICKER FLESH
16 EVER BLOOMING
17 EVER BEARING
18 LEAF: SIZE, SHAPE, COLOR
19 SKIN: SMOOTH, PUBESCENT, COLOR, UNIFORMITY
20 ROOTS: EDIBLE, DROUGHT RESISTANT, VIGOR
21 COOKING QUALITIES
22 NEW USES
23 STORAGE QUALITIES
24 ADAPTABILITY TO FREEZING
25 UNIFORMITY
26 LENGTH OF GROWING SEASON
27 ADAPTABILITY TO ONE SECTION
28 ADAPTABILITY TO GREENHOUSE GROWTH

The fact that each character must be evaluated separately is an indication that it may take several generations to bring one character to perfection and several additional generations to develop some other character. It is important, therefore, to try to evaluate all characters in each generation and make selections of those plants which show more progress toward the desired perfection in all characters.

The reason this separate evaluation of each character is being emphasized is that there are times when a new variety may appear to be very desirable, but one character which might have been overlooked has a degree of undesirability which makes all the other characters of less value, and may prevent acceptance in the trade.

VI

How to Recognize Undesirable Characters

THERE ARE some plant characters which are so undesirable that they alone may prevent the acceptance of a new variety. On the other hand, there are some undesirable characters which have been accepted because of the unusual value of other characters. Roses, for example, are appreciated universally even though they have thorns.

In general, thorniness is an undesirable characteristic. As in the case of blackberries, raspberries, roses, and other plants which bear thorns, we have learned to live with the prickly parts because we like the fruit and flowers so well. It is self-evident, however, that varieties of these plants without thorns would be more widely accepted, especially if the fruits or flowers were of equal value with those thorny kinds which we have been growing.

PLANTS MAY DEVELOP DISEASE-RESISTANT STRAINS

Certainly, susceptibility to prevalent diseases is an undesirable character which might outshadow all the good characters. There is always the possibility, however, that this susceptibility might not show up in some climates or in some states, often due to the fact that the disease has not yet been introduced into that section. For that reason, it is always wise to have a new variety tested in as many places as possible.

As has already been suggested, if you have a new variety which has so many desirable characters that its susceptibility to disease is the only undesirable feature, it is possible that you might discover some individual plants which have a resistance to the disease. Those plants might be a new strain of your new variety which could be introduced. Certainly, it is a possibility which should be explored if *susceptibility to disease* is the only undesirable characteristic you see.

In the same way, *susceptibility to common insect* pests is undesirable. A plant that succumbs to light frost probably would not be accepted in the trade. One easily *injured by hot weather* would not have universal acceptance. A plant whose fruit cracks on ripening would need to have further work done on it in order to discover some individual seedlings which have fruit that does not crack.

SOME FRUIT PLANTS ARE ACCEPTABLE FOR THEIR BLOSSOMS

If the fruit has an unpleasant flavor, that would undoubtedly rule out the new plant as a fruit producer. There is always the possibility, of course, that there might be some other part, such as the blossoms, which would have a use of sufficient importance to make people want the plant regardless of the fruit.

Those varieties which give a very small yield probably could not be sold to seedsmen or nurserymen if there were other varieties available which gave a better yield.

A fruit plant which is irregular in setting its fruit would not be worthy of introduction; consequently, the effort should be to search for individual plants which set their fruit *uniformly at a desirable time.*

Uneven ripening of fruit might be undesirable unless the plant could be classified as ever-bearing.

Fruit with warty or rough skin does not sell well on the market, and probably those who grow the fruit for their own use would not like it as well as other varieties which have fruit with smooth skin.

Fruits with too many seeds are undesirable. Seediness is an undesirable characteristic.

Fruit with a thick rind probably should be ruled out.

Certainly, a plant that is a weak grower would not find wide acceptance.

UNDESIRABLE CHARACTERS ARE EASILY OVERLOOKED

At times, many years ago when I was working with Mr. Burbank, he and I would walk through his plum orchard where thousands of new varieties were being tested. If the branch on which a beautiful fine-flavored plum grew had thorns or indicated susceptibility to sun scald, or any of the other characters which are undesirable in fruit trees, Mr. Burbank rejected the fruit entirely and eventually cut out the cion on which it grew. In other words, the desirability of the fruit alone was not enough to warrant introduction.

Fifteen Undesirable Characters

To summarize, here are fifteen characters, any one of which may make a new variety worthless:

1 THORNINESS	7 FRUIT AN UNPLEASANT FLAVOR
2 SUSCEPTIBILITY TO COMMON PESTS	8 VERY SMALL YIELD
	9 IRREGULAR IN SETTING FRUIT
3 SUSCEPTIBILITY TO PREVAILING DISEASES	10 RIPENS UNEVENLY
	11 WARTY OR ROUGH SKIN
4 PLANT SUCCUMBS TO LIGHT FROST	12 TOO MANY SEEDS
	13 THICK RIND
5 PLANT EASILY INJURED BY HOT WEATHER	14 WEAK GROWER
	15 BARK SUBJECT TO SUN SCALD
6 FRUIT CRACKS IN RIPENING	

TRY TO DETERMINE THE DEGREE OF UNDESIRABILITY

Inasmuch as there are degrees of undesirability, it is wise, of course, to try to determine the *degree* in the seedling you are studying. If the new plant is better in some important characteristics, a slightly undesirable character might not prevent its introduction. But if the degree of that undesirability were great, that alone might prevent its introduction.

In determining the degree of undesirability, it will be wise to get the opinions of as many others as possible. The opinions of nurserymen and seedsmen are unusually valuable in this connection because they know what it is that makes a new variety sell or prevents its sale. After all, if the new variety cannot be sold, there is no purpose in keeping it unless you want to use it for future experiments, particularly in connection with hybridizing, in the hope that the undesirable character may be minimized or eliminated entirely. *It is highly important not to overlook the undesirable characters.*

VII

How to Test a New Variety

AFTER YOU have a variety whose characters you have evaluated to the extent that you believe it is worthy of introduction, the next job is to test it thoroughly under varying conditions in order to be sure it will continue to reproduce plants of the type you believe will be in demand.

TEST PLANTS UNDER DIFFERENT CONDITIONS

If possible, grow or have grown some plants under as many conditions as you can arrange for, such as:

1. Different types of soil, including muck, sand, gravel, and loam
2. Several types of climate, including hot, dry, moist, cool, temperate
3. Short season, long season, medium season
4. Disease-infested soil
5. Insect-infested location
6. Rodent-infested area

You will, of course, study the effect on each character under each of the tested conditions and make careful records of the result. Certainly, if your plant grows under all these conditions and produces desirable, useful parts, it would classify as "extra good." On the other hand, it may grow successfully under certain conditions which are quite common and still be worthy of introduction even though it does not thrive under certain other conditions. There is a demand for plants which will grow under certain conditions and may not thrive under other conditions.

The principal purpose of testing your variety is to become thoroughly familiar with all of its characteristics, in order that you may provide the nurseryman or seedsman with complete information when you offer it to him.

You can undoubtedly get assistance in testing new varieties not only from your friends, but possibly also from the agricultural experiment station in your state or the

United States Department of Agriculture, Washington, D. C.; and perhaps from florists, nurserymen, and seedsmen.

How to Multiply Your New Variety

If the plant with which you are working is commonly grown from seed (for example, peas and beans), all you will need do is to plant some of the seeds of your new variety to increase your stock.

On the other hand, if it is one of those plants which is commonly reproduced from some other part of the plant; such as, bulbs, roots, or shoots, then it will be necessary to increase the stock by *vegetative reproduction*.

To get extra plants of a strawberry, you merely use those which are reproduced by *runners* from the new variety you have selected.

Stems or shoots arising from the underground portion of a plant are commonly called *suckers*. These are used to reproduce such plants as raspberries, loganberries, chrysanthemums, and others. The method known as *layering* is commonly used for reproducing black raspberries, rhododendrons, roses, and others. Tuberous plants such as potatoes and dahlias may be reproduced by planting the *tubers*.

The *corms* of crocus and the *bulbs* of gladiolus, onions, daffodils, hyacinths, tulips, and lilies should come true to the variety.

To reproduce a variety of cactus, you merely plant one of the sections of the stem which in some varieties appear to be very large leaves, but the cacti in general do not have leaves except when they first come through the ground.

How to Propagate Woody Plants

Hibiscus and other woody plants may be propagated by cuttings, air layering or marcottage, division, budding, and grafting. Plant specialists of the University of Florida make the following suggestions for multiplying woody plants.

CUTTINGS—Most varieties of hibiscus can be readily propagated by softwood cuttings. Tip cuttings of half-ripened wood, taken from May through July, will usually give best results. Cuttings will usually root in about six weeks and the plants produced from them will generally begin to flower in about nine months.

The leaf-bud cutting method is used for increasing rare varieties where there is a shortage of propagating material. It is now standard nursery procedure to grow the rooted cuttings to saleable size in containers; such as, pots, cypress boxes, or cans. They may be lined out in the nursery row, however, and later handled as "balled and burlapped" plants.

AIR LAYERING OR MARCOTTAGE—Woody plants that are difficult to root by cuttings can usually be increased readily by air layering or marcottage. A recently-developed method, which involves the use of a moisture-proof rubber plastic wrapper, has greatly improved the ease and efficiency of this method of propagation. Branches about one-half inch or larger in diameter are girdled at a point approximately 12 to 18 inches below the tip, by removing a strip of bark from one-half to one inch long. A ball of moist sphagnum moss 5 to 6 inches in length and 3 to 4 inches in diameter is placed over the girdled area, wrapped with a sheet of moisture-proof rubber plastic wrapper, and tied securely at each end with either rubber bands or string.

Fasten a piece of newspaper or wrapping paper loosely over the wrapper to prevent the sphagnum from overheating and birds from picking holes in it. Roots will be formed in the sphagnum moss, usually within six or eight weeks. The branch can then be cut off below where the roots have formed and set out as a new plant.

ROOTSTOCKS—Many woody plants are benefited by budding or grafting onto a vigorous, strong-growing rootstock. Any variety which experience has shown is easy to root, is strong-growing, and is tolerant to injury by rootknot and the root-rot fungus, would be satisfactory as a root-stock.

BUDDING—Shield-budding is the method most used and has given best results when performed in the spring; however, it may be done at any time during the year when the bark will slip readily. An inverted-T incision is made in the rootstock 2 to 3 inches from the ground. The bud is cut in the form of a shield, about an inch long, and inserted in the incision in the stock. It is tied in place with either rubber budding strips or budding tape or raffia.

TIP CUTTINGS—Tip cuttings should be taken when the wood is about half hardened (July-August-September). A box 7 to 9 inches deep and provided with good drainage is filled to within 2 inches of the top with clean, sharp sand. The cuttings with three leaves intact are plunged into the sand at an angle, so that the leaves lie almost flat on the surface. A cheesecloth cover is provided and the box is set in a shady place and watered every day through the cheesecloth.

Rooting may be hastened by treating the cuttings with one of the root-inducing substances. The simplest to use are those with a talc base. The butt-end of the cutting is dampened with water, plunged into the powder, and the excess removed by tapping sharply against the top of the container.

Cuttings may root in six weeks and be ready for potting or planting. Rooted cuttings should be *protected* for the first few months from intense cold or sun until their root system is established. If they can be kept in a greenhouse or cold-frame, they will produce a flush of growth early in the spring before plants in the open have started to grow, thus gaining half a season's growth.

Plants propagated by cuttings will come true to the variety from which they are taken, except in cases where the plant itself may show considerable color variation. In this case, the cutting may follow one of the variations.

GRAFTING—A quick way to bring a new variety into large size is to *graft it on an old root system*. The root system may be an unwanted variety, a seedling grown for that purpose, an old plant that year after year fails to bloom properly, or a vigorous rooted cutting grown for use as stock.

Camellias may be grafted at any time during the year

when the stock is dormant. Summer grafts are risky because of the succulent nature of the growth. They may be killed during the cold weather because they may not have hardened enough to withstand the cold of winter in the open. However, half a season's growth may be gained in this manner.

The stock is cut off smoothly a few inches above the surface of the ground and, depending upon its size, is split once or even twice with a chisel. If the trunk forks at the ground, both limbs may be used. The butt end of the cion (a tip cutting of vigorous growth of the previous summer) is cut to a long tapering wedge slightly thicker on one edge. This is inserted, with the thick edge outside, in the cut or cleft in the stump which is held open with a grafting tool or a screwdriver.

The growing area of a woody plant is between the bark and the wood and is known as the "cambium layer." To form a perfect union, the cambium layers of the stock and cion must coincide exactly. If the stump is quite small, pencil size for instance, only one cion is put in. If it is ¾ of an inch in diameter, a cion may be put in at each side of the cleft. If still larger, a cion may be inserted at each of two or more clefts which are cut at angles to each other. Small stocks may have to be tied with a string to hold the cion tightly in place, and very large stocks wedged open to prevent crushing the cion. After the graft has been made, the whole is covered with clean soil up to the leaves on the cion, or packed with green sphagnum moss.

A wide-mouthed glass jar is then inverted over the graft and shaded with a piece of burlap or some Spanish moss. When the union is made and growth starts on the cion, the glass jar is removed. Growth up to three feet or more, or even flower buds, may be expected from a graft on a large stump. A variety grown from a graft may be expected to be the same as that from which the cion was taken, but frequently variations appear that were not found previously.

SOURCES OF INFORMATION ON PROPAGATION

If you do not happen to be familiar with the technique of grafting, you may get complete instructions by writing to the United States Department of Agriculture, Washing-on, D. C., and asking for Farmers' Bulletin No. 1567, entitled the "Propagation of Trees and Shrubs." It clearly describes and illustrates the technique for vegetative reproduction of all types of trees and shrubs.

Another good bulletin to have on hand is Bulletin No. 137 of the Agricultural Experiment Station, Gainesville, Florida, entitled "Propagation of Ornamental Plants." If you do not live in Florida, it probably will be necessary to pay a fee for this bulletin, but it will be worth its small cost.

If you are interested in the vegetative propagation of citrus fruits, the Florida Experiment Station has another bulletin on that type of work—Bulletin No. 139.

Other helpful bulletins published by the United States Department of Agriculture are the following:

Farmers' Bulletin No. 471, entitled "Grape Propagation, Pruning, and Training."

No. 1123, "Growing and Planting Hardwood Seedlings."

No. 1171, "Growing Annual Flowering Plants."

No. 1369, "Bridge Grafting."

No. 1501, "Nut Tree Propagation."

Department of Agriculture leaflet 173, "The Bud-graft Method of Propagating Vinifera Grape Varieties on Rootstocks."

If you are interested in developing new varieties of plants, it would pay you to get these various bulletins and, at the same time, ask for a complete list of agriculture bulletins, for there may be others which will interest you.

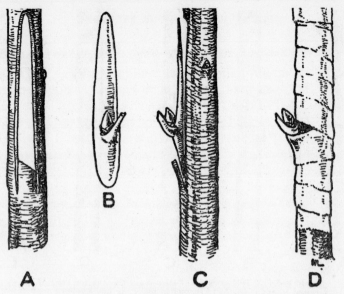

A simple and useful form of plate bud. A, Stock prepared by paring off a piece of bark, exposing the wood; B, bud cut similar to that for ordinary shield budding; C, bud in place; D, completed operation. Bud wrapped with waxed muslin

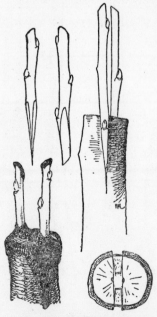

Cleft graft. Scions prepared, set in place, and waxed

Stock top removed with a sloping cut just above the bud. Ordinarily this is done the following spring about the time growth starts

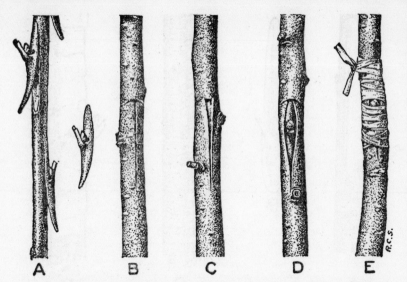

Shield bud. A, Bud stick; B, T-shaped cut through the bark of the stock;
C, bark raised to admit the bud; D, bud in place; E, bud wrapped with raffia

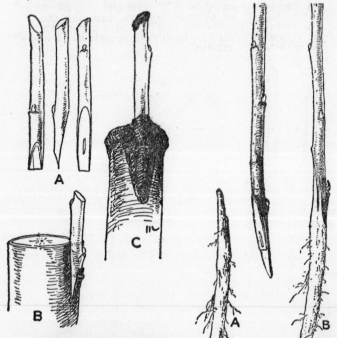

Bark graft. A, Scions
made by slanting cuts without
a shoulder; B, stock prepared
by taking out a piece of bark
to admit the scion; C, the
complete graft with all the
cuts waxed

Whip graft. A, Scion and
stock prepared; B, fitted together;
C, wrapped with waxed twine

VIII

Official Testing of New Varieties

I F YOU discover or develop a new variety of rose, you may have the benefit of official testing by the All-America Rose Selections, Inc. This is a group of rose specialists organized for the purpose of testing roses which may be new varieties. They also study other plants. It has been in operation since 1938, and the secretary is W. Ray Hastings, Box 675, Harrisburg, Pennsylvania. Mr. Hastings explained the testing in a letter to me as follows:

"Anyone may enter his varieties for pre-introductory testing. We solicit and do everything we can to obtain entries of varieties really believed different and superior to similar kinds or colors already in commerce. Meritorious varieties, preferably widely adapted but which may be regionally recommended or awarded, certainly should be entered in these trials. Their recommendation as All-America winners assures co-operative promotion on the part of the horticultural trade.

FLOWERS AND VEGETABLES ARE TESTED

"At present, we have nineteen official rose judges responsible for the nineteen official rose test gardens of AARS. There are six additional demonstration gardens where these roses are also grown, judged, and scored over the two-year testing period. However, their scores are not averaged with those of the official judges since such might give over-balanced judgment for some sections of the country. We have twenty-one official vegetable judges and trial grounds; we have twenty-three flower seed judges.

WINNING VARIETIES ARE PUBLICIZED

"Publicity release material on the new winners goes to all sizable and known publications dealing with gardens in any form. These include home and garden magazines,

farm journals, trade publications, radio, television and all
sizable newspapers in America. Horticultural publications abroad also use this release material. So, many
millions of subscribers may know of these outstanding
varieties the first season of introduction.

"With a plant vegetatively reproduced and patentable,
such as roses, the originator or introducer should certainly
take advantage of these trials.

"Since nothing is said to hurt any variety which may
have gone through the trials and failed to win, the scores
and comments of the judges should be very helpful in
breeding work and help determine whether to introduce
the variety or not. If it should win recommendation, it
would certainly bring multiplied royalties through the
tremendously increased sales and without any appreciable
gamble on the part of the patent owner.

"It is hoped that other horticultural products may
have the advantage of such pre-introductory testing and
rating in the not distant future. You may be sure that
representatives of plant societies and others particularly
interested in such as gladioli, dahlias, lilies, perennials,
small fruits, fruits, camellias, evergreens, etc., have asked
us to include their favorite or commercial kinds in All-
America testing. Naturally, it takes some financing for
the operating and inspecting of a number of trial grounds
over the country (and we include Canada in the vegetable
and flower seed trials) and it would be necessary for
practically an entirely new setup for each class of plant
materials. Rose judges may not be qualified for iris
judges or other kinds."

When you have a new variety of any kind ready to be
tested, it would be very wise to write a letter to Mr. Hastings
and tell him what you have and ask him for the conditions
under which it may be thoroughly tested.

How New Varieties Are Publicized

The following is a quotation from the New England
Homestead which shows how the All-America varieties are

publicized. Publicity is sent to all periodicals which go to people who are interested in the varieties just made available. Here's what the New England Homestead said about All-America selections of vegetables:

"A singular honor has been granted to Dr. A. F. Yeager of the University of New Hampshire. The All-America Vegetable selection judges have picked two of his discoveries as worthy of recognition for All-America honors.

"His New Hampshire Midget watermelon was one of two gold medal winners this year. This is only the fifth vegetable since 1935 to attain gold medal ranking. Yeager's Granite State Muskmelon won a bronze medal from the judges.

"Other vegetables selected this year were Iochief, a new hybrid sweet corn; Surecrop, a hybrid cucumber; and O-S Cross, the first hybrid cabbage.

"The New Hampshire Midget watermelon is a small early maturing oval melon. Under favorable conditions it ripens in 65 days from seed and is especially recommended for the northern short growing season sections where large melons will not mature or develop good eating quality. It is light or gray-green in color with narrow irregular darker striping. Its average weight is only two and one-half pounds. It is about six inches through, but the rind is very thin and the bright red flesh is solid and sweet. Sizable seeds are black, distinguishing it from the White Mountain with many small brown seeds which has been called "Midget" erroneously. The vine is rather small but very fruitful of melons which are adapted for the refrigerator. They are ordinarily served half a melon per person. This is desirable for home garden and local market use. It can be shipped if handled in muskmelon crates.

"The Granite State Muskmelon is a sectional recommendation for the northern short growing season. Compared chiefly with Honey Rock, Granite State was found to be earlier, slightly more oval in shape, with more open and smoother netting. The flesh is of lighter orange color, firm, thick, of high quality and with a smaller seed cavity.

"Fruits average five to five and one-half by four to four and one-half inches in size and two to two and one-half pounds in weight. Because of extra earliness and rather small fruits borne in a concentrated period of time, it is a northern melon. Productive vines are rather small and compact with abundant small leaves, resistant to downy mildew. This home and market melon ripens in about 70 days and the stem separates from the fruit on maturity.

"The Iochief Hybrid Sweetcorn was developed by Dr. E. S. Haber of Iowa State College. It is of the same maturing season as Goldencross Bantam. Its ears are from nine to ten inches long with 16 to 18 rows of exceptionally deep golden grains giving 40% cutting weight. The silk color inside the husk is a very light brown. Leaves are broad and medium green. The stalks are medium green and heavy-wind resistant. The tassels are large with yellow anthers and abundant pollen. Plants average one short tiller or sucker and are somewhat resistant to heat and drought. Iochief has excellent flavor and tenderness and a heavy yield.

"The O-S Cross Cabbage is the first hybrid cross of this family. Exceptional uniformity in extra large size and maturity with huge yields of this vigorous drumhead Succession type cabbage demand attention and admiration. They weigh from eight to ten pounds per head and carry fine color. This cabbage stands out for fresh, kraut, and canning uses. It is a broad, low-growing, short-stemmed plant with blue outer leaves and a rather light green head. For home and canning uses, it is rather large for present market demands.

"The Surecrop Hybrid Cucumber brings unusually vigorous vines and increased yields, resistant to mosaic and downy mildew. This White Spine type for slicing holds its dark green color well after picking. Eight to

1. THIS IS THE BURBANK JULY ELBERTA PEACH DEVELOPED BY
LUTHER BURBANK MANY YEARS AGO. IT IS THE PARENT OF THE STARKING
DELICIOUS PEACH SHOWN IN PLATE 2

American Fruit Grower

2. STARKING DELICIOUS PEACH PRODUCED ON ONE LIMB OF A BURBANK JULY PEACH TREE. DESCRIBED AS EARLIEST OF QUALITY YELLOW FREE-STONE PEACHES, IT RIPENS TEN DAYS BEFORE GOLDEN JUBILEE; SEVEN DAYS BEFORE RED HAVEN PEACH. STARK BROTHERS PAID $10,000 FOR LIMB ON WHICH THIS BUD SPORT GREW

nine inches long by two and one-half inches wide, the fruits are blunt ended and are ready for picking in about 58 days from seed. The flesh is white, crisp, tender, of unusually good flavor and very uniform. Surecrop bears over a long season so is especially desirable for home garden use. It was developed in Colorado."

IX

You Have the Right to Name a New Variety

ONE OF THE real pleasures many people get from developing new varieties is the opportunity for naming their new plants. If no plant has heretofore been named for the inventor, he may give it his own name. Many new varieties are named in that way and it is a real thrill and a tremendous satisfaction to the introducer to know that his name is perpetuated in this splendid way.

Some have named new varieties for their favorite hero. Others have created original names. Probably one of the best kinds of names is that which indicates some quality of the new plant. The word "early" would be appropriate in the name of a new variety which produces its useful parts earlier than others. The word "prolific" would be appropriate in the name of a plant which produces its useful parts more abundantly. In some cases, the naming of the new plant is left to the seedsman who introduces it. In other cases, the friends of the inventor suggest a name.

As an illustration of some of the personal names that have been used with new varieties, the following are names of roses: Charlotte Armstrong, Katherine T. Marshall, Blanche Mallerin, and Mark Sullivan.

The following are illustrations of names which indicate qualities of the new varieties: Mastodon strawberry, Double Red Delicious, Abundance plum, Silver Lustre gladiolus, Gold gladiolus, Bonfire gladiolus, Powder Puff chrysanthemum, Golden Hours chrysanthemum.

An admirer of Queen Elizabeth introduced a new white gladiolus and named it "Elizabeth, the Queen." Another gladiolus is named "Florence Nightingale." Still another one is "General Eisenhower."

It really is a great thrill to name a new variety which you have discovered or developed and that thrill will continue as long as you live.

X

Keep Careful Records

IT IS POSSIBLE to patent a new plant just the same as a new machine or a new chemical. Furthermore, it is wise to have a new plant patented in order to prevent nurserymen and seedsmen, other than the one to whom you sell your new variety, from propagating and distributing it. If you sell your new variety to an introducer, he will pay you either a flat fee or a royalty on all he sells. That is why a patent is important.

If you contemplate getting a patent, it will be necessary to supply accurate information regarding the variety. For that reason and for other obvious reasons, it is important to keep careful records of all of your work in connection with discovering, propagating, or developing new varieties.

KEEP THESE SEVEN TYPES OF RECORDS

It probably would be best to use a loose leaf record book in order that you might expand your records as needed. Probably seven types of records will be important as follows:

1 Parentage
2 Cultural methods tested
3 Climate testings
4 Other tests made
5 Characters of the plants saved
6 Characters of plants discarded
7 Seedsmen and nurserymen to whom the plant was offered

(1) Under the heading of *Parentage*, you will want to record the facts you know about the parents of the plant and its methods of reproduction. For example, if it is a plant you found in the fields, woods, or an orchard, you will, of course, assume that it is a chance seedling. On the other hand, if you produced it by crossing certain varieties and then planted the seeds, you will know the parentage and will, of course, make an accurate record.

(2)   Under the heading of *Culture*, you will record not only the different types of soil in which the plant has been tested, but the results of each test. You will make a record of the cultivation technique used and, if you used more than one method, you will record the results of each type. You will also record the amount of water supplied if special irrigating methods were used.

(3)   Under the heading of *Climate*, you should make a record of high and low temperatures and humidity. If tests were made in different parts of the country, you should describe the climate in each place accurately.

(4)   Under the heading of *Other Tests*, you should record all of the circumstances under which the plant was tested and the specific results, both good and bad. The record of tests should reveal the locality and those conditions under which the plant will thrive best and those conditions under which it does not thrive.

(5, 6)   In Chapters V and VI, you were told about the various *characters*, and you should make a record of the characters of those plants which are saved, as well as those which are discarded. Indicate in some way, if you can, the degree to which each character was developed.

(7)   Under the heading of *Distribution*, you should list those seedsmen to whom you offered the plant and their replies. It might even be wise to file their letters as a part of this record so that you may refer to them in the future in order to estimate which seedsmen would be most likely to buy a new variety when you have others to sell.

XI

How to Select an Introducer for Your New Variety

IN ORDER to select the dealer who is likely to have the greatest success in introducing your new variety, it is important, of course, for you to study catalogues of as many seedsmen and nurserymen as you can. What you want most to know about each one is the success he has had with the type of plant you have to introduce. You want to know whether or not he is a good advertiser. You want to try to find out, if you can, whether he is the type of seedsman who will keep the stock pure or whether he will be inclined to develop new strains to be introduced later as his own varieties.

The first step is to look over all the advertisements of seedsmen and nurserymen you can find in various farm and garden publications. It probably would be wise to send for the catalogues of each one or, at any rate, it would be wise to send for the catalogues of those who sell the type of plant you have for introduction.

PICK A GOOD ADVERTISER

After these catalogues are assembled, it is then important to study them carefully in order to reach a conclusion as to which dealer seems to be the best salesman as indicated by his catalogue and his descriptions therein. If, for example, the seedsman merely lists the name of each variety and the price, you would naturally conclude that this selling literature was not prepared by an expert and probably will not sell as large a quantity.

On the other hand, if the reading matter is very interesting and of the type which will make people want to try the varieties offered, you then will conclude that this man understands selling and will do a better job for you.

The size of the catalogue, the number of colored pictures in it and its general appearance are indicators of the suc-

cessful distributor. The number of times you see a seedsman's advertising in various publications is an indication
of his sales ability.

In order to learn something of the reliability of a
seedsman, it will be necessary to ask the opinions of various
people who know dealers in the line that interests you. You
probably could not get an answer to a letter written to an
experiment station or the Department of Agriculture, but
if you visit with some of the men in those institutions, they
probably will give you some ideas which they would not be
willing to put into a letter. In the same way, some commercial growers who buy large quantities of seeds might have
valuable opinions which they would be willing to give you.

Write a Letter Before Submitting Samples

After you have selected the one you believe will be the
best dealer, the next step is to write a letter explaining what
you have to offer and ask if he would be interested in receiv-
ing samples. When you send the samples, it is important
to ask for an offer for introduction and for comments on the
variety.

If the first dealer to whom you submit your new variety
does not decide to introduce it, send it to some other. As
long as you have confidence in your new plant, keep trying
various seedsmen or nurserymen until you find the one who
is ready to do your new plant justice.

If comments from the various seedsmen who do not
decide to introduce your new variety indicate some undesirable characters, perhaps it will then be necessary for you
to try to eliminate the undesirable features by further hybridization or selection or both. The point is, you must not
be discouraged by refusals to purchase. When you finally
find the right introducer, he is likely to be enthusiastic about
your variety, and you can then forget all the unfavorable
comments you received from others.

Don't Let One Refusal Discourage You

There are a number of reasons why a firm might not be
interested in buying a certain new variety. One of the

chief reasons is that it may be such as to compete seriously with a variety they are already selling. For example, a nurseryman might have a large stock of a certain variety of rose which he would not want to discard. It might be that your variety of rose so outshines the one he is now selling that he fears that he would have his present stock left on his hands if he accepted yours.

Occasionally, a seedsman or nurseryman may have a certain type of customer to whom he thinks your variety would not appeal, whereas there might be another nurseryman who has just been waiting for a variety like yours.

It you have a new variety in which you have confidence, don't stop trying to find an introducer until you have "made the rounds."

XII

You Can Grow Thousands
of New Varieties

IT ISN'T NECESSARY to wait until you discover something new growing in your garden, in the fields, or in the nearby woods. You can develop new varieties any time you wish. Plant 1,000 seeds of each of the following types of fruits: grapes, raspberries, blackberries, blueberries, plums, peaches, apricots, apples, pears, quinces, and strawberries. You will have several thousand different seedlings, for each fruit seed produces a new kind.

Seeds of many fruits require "after-ripening" at a temperature of about 40–45° F for about six weeks, if good germination is to be obtained. The seeds should be stratified in moist sand or other suitable material and subjected to the above conditions by placing them in artificial refrigeration or out of doors during the winter when temperatures are 40 to 45° F for the specified time.

When "after-ripening" is completed, these seeds may be planted in flats in a greenhouse or in boxes in the window of a warm room; or if you plant them out-of-doors, they should be in flats or boxes where you can control the weeds more easily. If you plant them in the garden or field, it will be difficult to keep down the weeds until the young plants get a start.

How to Get 11,000 New Varieties of Flowers

If you prefer to work with flowers, plant seeds of those flowers commonly reproduced by tubers, bulbs, and corms. Plant 1,000 seeds each of: tuberous-rooted begonias, lilies, tulips, gladioli, amaryllis, anemones, callas, gloxinias, hyacinths, trigridias, and iris and you should have 11,000 new varieties of flowers from which to make selection in the hope of finding some new ones which are better than those we already have.

If you prefer to work with those plants which are commonly reproduced by seeds, it would be wise to cross-pollenize two or more varieties and then save the resulting seeds. In this way, you should get new types rather than a continuation of the old variety. Instructions as to how to cross-pollenize will be found in Chapter XV. The plants resulting from cross-pollination are referred to as "hybrids." Hybrids quite commonly have what is often referred to as "hybrid vigor." They usually are thrifty plants, although there may be some which are not.

SELECT CAREFULLY FROM YOUR NEW VARIETIES

Obviously, after you get your thousands of seedling plants, the next job is to make selection of those which seem to be better than what we already have, or of those which seem to be going in the direction of plants with desirable characters. Those plants may then be pollenized later and, among the resulting hybrids, you may find some which will be nearly or entirely up to the standard you have set in the beginning.

Professionals who make a business of hybridization sometimes make crosses generation after generation. In other words, they may grow 5 or 6, or even 10 or 12 new generations of plants, each one hybridized, before they find just what they are looking for.

If you want to develop new plant varieties, it will be wise to grow thousands. If you grow only hundreds, it may take many more years. If you grow thousands, you may be able to find good new varieties in one, two, three, or four years.

THIS EXPERIENCE SHOWS THE JOY OF A HYBRIDIZER

The real pleasure of hybridization and selection of new varieties is indicated in a letter written by Elizabeth A. Briggs who has been hybridizing gladioli for 30 years. Her following letter indicates not only the method of bringing about new varieties, but the pleasure:

"Thirty-six years ago, my son and I planted our first gladioli with the idea of making it a commercial venture.

It was not until six years later that I began hybridizing, although I had been thinking very seriously about it all that time.

"To begin with, I knew that I must gather together in my garden all the best varieties then in existence for my *foundation stock*.

"The best hybridizers of that time were A. E. Kunderd, Indiana; Richard Diener, California, and the Pfitzer family in Germany. Accordingly, I sent to each of them for their best, in all the various colors.

"The little Primulinus species, the only pure yellow then in existence, had been discovered only recently in Africa by the English bridge builders near the Victoria Falls and brought home to England where it was catalogued by an English gladiolus grower. Mr. Kunderd had purchased some bulbs of the species and added them to his list. Luckily, I bought some of them.

"This species produced a small hooded blossom about the size of a silver quarter. It was not much to look at, but it had that pure daffodil color that was much wanted and then lacking in the gladiolus. To mate with this precious miniature yellow, I bought one bulb of Golden Measure from Kelway's in England. It was a large yellow with a rather muddy color, priced at $25 per bulb.

A Sensational New Gladiolus in Six Generations

"After six generations of line breeding with this seemingly ill-mated pair, I was presented with an eight-inch pure yellow glad of exquisite form. Since then, many other fine yellow glads have appeared in my garden. Besides the clear yellow varieties, there are several outstanding orange and copper colored ones that are even more attractive than pure yellow, and all are from this same line of breeding.

"Not only has the Primulinus species given me grand varieties in yellow and orange, but these offspring are all remarkably healthy and prolific.

"If you could visit my garden at blossom time, you would see more pink glads than those of any other colors. The pink ones are my favorites. These have all been line bred from Diener's lovely Mr. W. H. Phipps and Pfitzer's Coryphee.

"It is too long a story to tell it all; this has been a pleasant journey. To many, it may seem like hard work, but to me the joy of it all far outweighs the total of work and fatigue. For many years, I have refused to call it work. To me it is play."

XIII

How to Patent a New Variety

FEDERAL LAWS recognize the importance of encouraging and protecting those who discover or invent new varieties of plants. The law reads as follows:

INVENTIONS PATENTABLE

"Any person who has invented or discovered any new and useful art, machine, manufacture, or composition of matter, or any new and useful improvements thereof, or who has invented or discovered and asexually reproduced any distinct and new variety of plant, other than a tuber-propagated plant, not known or used by others in this country before his invention or discovery thereof, and not patented or described in any printed publication in this or any foreign country before his invention or discovery thereof, or more than one year prior to his application, and not in public use or on sale in this country for more than one year prior to his application, unless the same is proved to have been abandoned, may, upon payment of the fees required by law, and other due proceeding had, obtain a patent therefor."

A New Wild Variety May Be Patented

Note that the law says "invented or discovered." That means if you find a seedling in the fields or woods, you can claim discovery and can patent the new variety for the purpose of obtaining a sale price or a royalty from the seedsman or nurseryman who introduces it. This patent, the same as all patents, lasts for 17 years.

Inasmuch as it costs quite a little money to obtain a patent, it usually is wise for the inventor to wait until he has found a seedsman or nurseryman who will introduce it and then arrange for the patent with an *assignment* to the introducer. The law provides for such assignment in the following words:

Assignment of patents and applications;
evidence of execution

"Every applicant for patent or any interest therein shall be assignable in law by an instrument in writing, and the applicant or patentee or his assigns or legal representatives may in like manner grant and convey an exclusive right under his application for patent to the whole or any specified part of the United States. An assignment, grant, or conveyance shall be void as against any subsequent purchaser or mortgagee for a valuable consideration, without notice unless it is recorded in the Patent Office within three months from the date thereof or prior to such subsequent purchase or mortgage.

"If any such assignment, grant, or conveyance of any application for patent shall be acknowledged before any notary public of the several States or Territories or the District of Columbia, or any commissioner of any court of the United States for any district or Territory, or before any secretary of legation or consular officer authorized to administer oaths or perform notarial acts under section 131 of Title 22, the certificate of such acknowledgment, under the hand and official seal of such notary or other officer, shall be prima facie evidence of the execution of such assignment, grant, or conveyance."

TUBER-PROPAGATED PLANTS ARE NOT PATENTABLE

You will undoubtedly be surprised at the phrase in the law which eliminates tuber-propagated plants. It is not easy to understand why they were excluded when the law was written. The chairman of the Patent Committee, however, did say this in his report to Congress: "This exception is made because this group alone among asexually reproduced plants is propagated by the same part of the plant that is sold as food."

The Committee Report further makes this statement:

"The term 'tuber' is used in its narrow horticultural sense as meaning a short thickened portion of an underground branch. It does not cover, for instance, bulbs, corms, stolons, and rhizomes."

The potato and the Jerusalem artichoke are the two plants which seem to be most important in this exclusion.

A PATENT ATTORNEY EXPLAINS THE PROCESS

One of my personal friends happens to be a patent attorney specializing in obtaining plant patents. I have talked with him many times on the subject and learn that patents are commonly obtained at the time when a new variety is bought by a seedsman or nurseryman, or when he obtains permission to introduce it on a royalty basis.

When someone writes to the attorney to ask for information about getting a new plant variety patented, he commonly answers them in a way to give them complete information about the process. Following is a typical letter written by him:

"The cost of filing an application for a plant patent will be $200 which includes our services, the first Government fee of $30 and the cost of making drawings, which are usually paintings, if color is a factor in the identification of your plant.

"If there is to be an assignment, the name of the person or company to whom the assignment runs should be given and, if it is a corporation, the State in which it is incorporated should be stated. The cost of assignment is $10.

"After the application is allowed, there will fall due a final Government fee of $30 payable within six months.

"In some unusual cases where the Patent Office finds reasons for rejecting or objection to the application for patent, there may be some additional expense to cover the work of making the necessary amendments, but this would not be incurred without first consulting you.

THESE CONDITIONS GOVERN THE GRANTING OF A PATENT

"In order to obtain a valid patent, it is necessary that the application be filed in the name of the inventor; that is, the person or persons who made the discovery or carried out the breeding procedure that resulted in the new variety.

"The principal conditions governing the grant of a patent are:

1 The plant must have characteristics that distinguish it from other varieties of the family to which it belongs.

2 The plant must have been reproduced asexually

and its novel characteristics proved to be maintained in its progeny.

3 The plant must not have been placed on sale to the public more than one year prior to the filing of the application for patent.

4 The application must precisely claim and describe the novel characteristics of the plant in such manner that the patent clearly distinguishes the plant from previously existing ones and must be accompanied by drawings in color, if color is a factor.

"If you desire to have us prepare and file an application for patent, we will send you a questionnaire that, in a general way, indicates some of the data that we should be able to provide and this should be executed in so far as its items relate to your plant, and returned to us.

A Sample Plant Must Be Supplied

"It is also necessary to send us a sample of the plant showing the novel characteristics on which reliance is to be had in obtaining the patent. In some cases, it is possible to make the necessary drawings from photographs but, usually, it is best to have them made from the plant.

"Plant patent applications must be filed in duplicate as they are subject to examination by both the Patent Office and the Department of Agriculture.

"Our usual terms are $100 with the order and the balance of the filing cost when the application is submitted to you for signature. Rummler, Rummler & Snow, 7 South Dearborn St., Chicago, Illinois."

In order for a plant to be patented, it must have some special characteristics which are different—presumably better than those same characteristics in other plants now available. In order that he might have complete information regarding all of the characters of the plant my friend, William Snow, asks each applicant to fill in the following form. It will be noted that spaces are provided in this form for information regarding the various characteristics:

PLANT PATENT
(Flower)

Parentage
Seedling or sport ....
If seedling, seed parent .... Pollen parent ....
If sport, name parent variety ....
Classification: Botanic (name strain) ....
It is the result of definite breeding efforts carried on by me or my
associates since ....
Have you reproduced this plant asexually from cuttings ....,
roots ...., buds ...., grafting ....
Flower
Blooming habit: Recurrent .... Continuous ....
Intermittent .... Spring .... Fall ....
Blooms: Once .... Early .... Midseason ....
Late .... Profusely .... Sparsely ....
Has a tendency to give a few blooms in Fall ....
Other habits ....
Size: Very large .... Medium ....
Borne: Singly .... Clusters ....
Shape: When first opens: Cup .... Flat .... High center ....
Petalage: Number .... Form .... Serrated ....
Inside petals .... Reverse side ....
Discoloration ....
Texture: Leathery .... Soft ....
Appearance: Shiny .... Satiny .... Velvety ....
Affected by wet or hot weather ....
Persistence (hang on and dry) ....
Disease resistant ....
Fragrance ....
Lasting quality: On plant .... As a cut flower ....
Bud
Size: ....
Form: Short .... With flat top ....
Long .... Pointed .... Urn .... Ovoid ....
Globular ....
Color: When sepals first divide ....
When petals begin to unfurl ....
Sepals: "Hooded" over bud .... Stand up .... Curl back ....
Spear-shaped .... Fall off ....
Calyx: Shape .... Funnel ....
Size: Large .... Broad .... Long ....
Does it split ....
Aspect: Smooth .... Hairy .... Glandular ....
Peduncle: Length .... Hairy ....
Plant
Form: Bush .... Height ....
Growth .... Vigorous .... Branching ....
Foliage
Quantity: Abundant .... Size of leaf ....
Texture: Leathery .... Glossy .... Smooth ....
Color: Upper side .... Lower side ....

Shape: ....
Petioles: Length ....
                Thorns .... Spines .... Prickles ....
Corms
    Color .... Size ....
Genital Organs
    Stamens, anthers .... Length .... Number ....
    Color .... Arrangement ....
    Pollen .... Color ....
    Styles: Number .... Length ....
    Ovaries ....
    Fertile ....
Fruit
    Shape: Round .... Ovoid .... Pear-shaped ....
                Oblong ....
    Color at maturity ....
Has the plant ever been offered for sale? .... When? ....
Has this plant ever been described to other persons? ....
    If so, when? ....
Has it been described in any publication? ....
    When ....
Name the variety it most resembles ....
Compare it with other varieties ....
Inventor's Full Name ....
Address ....
Interest assigned to ....
If corporation, State of corporation ....
If partnership, full name of partners
                ....
                ....

31 CHARACTERS CLAIMED TO BE DIFFERENT IN PATENTED PLANTS

It is interesting and helpful to know the characters claimed by those who have already patented plants. The following list is not up-to-date by any means, but it is of sufficient length to indicate the importance of the various characters:

1. Color in 58 patents
2. Shape in 25 patents
3. Vigor of plant in 17
4. Productiveness in 13
5. Size in 18
6. Ripening period in 15
7. Fragrance in 10
8. Freedom from thorns in 7
9. Special or unique foliage in 13
10. Flavor in 5
11. Resistance to disease in 5
12. Firmness of flesh in 5
13. Everblooming habit in 7
14. Canning quality in 3
15. Shipping quality in 2
16. Smooth surface in 1
17. Freestone in 1
18. Size of seed in 1
19. Thin shell nut in 1
20. Self fertile flower in 1
21. New "Brambleberry" in 1
22. Absence of seeds in 1
23. Superior grafting qualities in 1
24. Heavy set of fruit in 1

25. Keeping quality of flowers
    in 5
26. Size and number of corms
    in 1
27. Ease of reproduction in 3

28. Special bud and flower de-
    velopment in 1
29. Persistence of color in 2
30. Prolific blossoms in 4
31. Resistance to cold in 2

On page 357 of the March, 1948, *National Geographic Magazine* begins an article on Plant Patents which is very interesting and helpful. With this article are color drawings of several varieties of fruits and flowers which were submitted to the Patent Office. When color is an important element in the new variety, the Government requires 3 colored paintings. The paint used must be some that does not fade. When the first patents were allowed, water color drawings or kodachrome photographs were accepted, but it was discovered that both of these fade and a search of patent records in the future could not be accurate for that reason.

TYPES OF PLANTS THAT CANNOT BE PATENTED

It has been emphasized by the Patent Office frequently that patents are not issued on seeds or vegetables or fruits, or on any plant that grows only from seed or on tuber-propagated plants. At the time the *National Geographic* article was written, more than 750 plant patents had been issued and nearly 75% of these were for roses. At least one new variety of gladiolus had been patented because of its pleasant odor.

This article reports the sale of a rose without thorns which was patented in 1942. The sale price was $10,000! Up to that time, that was the highest price ever paid for a new variety of plant. The rose was patented by A. F. Watkins of the Dixie Rose Nursery.

When new plants are sold on a royalty basis, the royalty quite often ranges from 5 to 20 cents per plant for every plant sold by the introducer.

This article also reports a sale price of $10,000 for rights to introduce a new variety of peach which was a sport found by J. Frank Smith of Arkansas on a July Elberta peach tree. The chief characteristic of the sport was that it ripened three weeks earlier than other peaches on the parent tree. It is evident that there is money to be made by developing new and useful varieties of plants.

XIV

Concerning Hybridization

THE NEW PLANT which grows from a seed resulting from the transfer of pollen from one variety to the flower on another variety is called a "hybrid." Closely related plants are more easily hybridized than others.

Plants are classified according to their characteristics. The largest classification is known as the "phylum." The seed plants, for example, make up a phylum which has the name Spermatophyta. The classification groups with which we are most concerned, however, are known as "genus," "species," and "variety." The genus usually includes two or more species. A species may contain any number of varieties.

At one time it was thought that plants could not be crossed unless they were both of the same species. However, specific and even generic crosses are now rather commonly made by plant breeders. Luther Burbank was able to cross two species of fruits: the apricot and the plum. The resulting hybrid is classified as a new kind of fruit, which he called the "plumcot." Without a doubt, however, it is easier to cross two plants of the *same species*.

How to Select the Parents

The preparation for hybridization includes a study of the characters possessed by each parent and the selection of parents to bring about desired characteristics in the new plant.

These characteristics cannot be accurately foretold, but what you desire is more likely to materialize if one or both parents have characters which are somewhat like the new characters you are seeking. For example, one parent might be inclined to early maturity. The other parent might be inclined to prolific production. If you wish to have both of these characters in the new plant, you are more likely to get them if you use one parent with the early maturing characteristic and another with the prolific characteristic than if you selected both parents for their prolific production.

It must be emphasized again that it is necessary to plant thousands of seeds in order to get a good new variety. Sometimes, it is true, a good new variety appears when only a few seeds are planted, but progress is more rapid if you work with larger numbers.

Recrossing May Be Necessary

After the seedlings appear, it is necessary, of course, to select those plants which are most nearly like what you want. If none of them is exactly what you want, it may be necessary to re-cross some of the *seedlings*. In that case, you select one seedling from among the hybrid plants which is more pronounced in early maturity than any of the others, and another hybrid which appears to be more prolific than any of the others. You cross these in the hope of intensifying both characters and often you will be rewarded.

On the other hand, if your selected hybrid appears to have sufficient earliness of maturity, it may be wise to cross it back onto the *parent* with prolific tendencies. This should intensify the prolificacy. In other words, a hybrid may be bred back to one of its parents or it may be crossed with a fellow hybrid.

$1,000 a Pound for Seed

The value of hybridization may be emphasized by the fact that the Department of Agriculture once reported a case in which a professional hybridizer was paid $1,000 a pound for seeds from hybridized potatoes. Potatoes do not bear seeds very often, and it would take many, many seeds to make a pound. With that knowledge, the $1,000 price is not too surprising.

XV

The Technique of Hybridization

POLLEN is generally recognized as a yellow dust produced in the anther of the flower which, when transferred to the stigma at the top of the pistil of the same flower or another flower of the same variety or the same species, fertilizes the ovules, and thus brings about the development of seeds. The pollen grain carries the male element; the ovule contains the female element.

From the pollen grain that lands on the stigmatic surface of the pistil, a pollen tube develops which grows down through the style into the ovary where the male element is released to unite with the female element in the ovule. The male and female elements or nuclei bring to this union or fertilization some of the hereditary units (chromosomes and genes) which control the characteristics of the parent plants. Thus, characteristics from the male parent are combined with those from the female parent.

The resulting offspring which come from the seeds thus formed may or may not be approximately the same as the parents, depending upon the type of plant. Hybrids of those plants which we commonly reproduce from seeds and which are naturally self-pollinated, such as peas and beans, are likely to be very much like the parents. On the other hand, hybrids of seed-propagated plants such as corn and squash which are naturally cross-pollinated and those plants which are commonly reproduced by vegetative methods, such as grafting, layering, bulbs, and so on, are likely to be quite different from the parents.

POLLINATION MAY BE SIMPLE

When we wish to bring about new varieties, the common method is to transfer the pollen from the anthers of one variety to the stigma of another. The technique of doing this sounds simple when explained and, in some cases, it is simple. In the case of other plants, there are technicalities which make it difficult or impossible to transfer successfully the pollen from one to the other.

The simplest method is merely to cut a flower from one plant when the pollen is ripe and brush the pollen on a flower of another plant. However, such a simple procedure is not usually reliable, if one desires to be certain of the parentage of the offspring.

WHEN TO POLLINATE

The pollen must be ripe at the same time the stigma is ready to receive it. If the pollen is not ripe, or if the stigma is not receptive, no cross will result. For that reason, it is important before cross pollinating to study carefully the flower parts on both parents in order to discover exactly when the pollen is ready and when the stigma is receptive.

When the pollen is ready, it is released from the little pollen sacs (the anthers) on the stamens of the flower. Therefore, if you pick a flower and tap it gently on a piece of paper, you will see the yellow dust on the paper if the pollen is ready for distribution. On the other hand, if you do not see any pollen, you may conclude that it is not yet time for the transfer—or else the time has passed.

Receptivity of the stigma is usually indicated by the presence of a sticky substance on its surface. This substance helps to hold the pollen which lands on the stigma and also hastens the germination of the pollen tube. In cases where the stigma is composed of two or more branches, these will usually be spread out when the stigmatic surfaces are receptive.

SOMETIMES POLLINATION IS DIFFICULT

There are some flowers whose blossoms are so small that it may be necessary to use a magnifying glass and tweezers in order to familiarize yourself with the plant parts and to discover the favorable time for transferring the pollen. In some cases, it may be necessary to pick the stamens from one flower with tweezers under the microscope, carry them on a watch crystal to the other flower, and

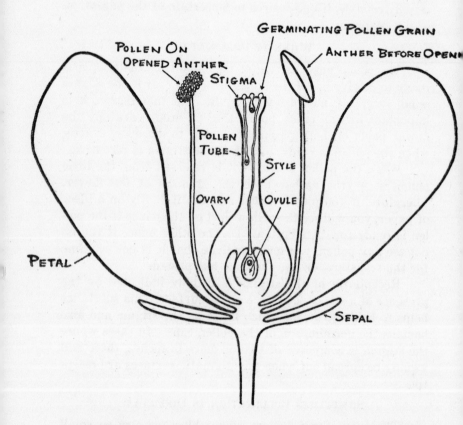

Diagram of the parts of a simple flower. When the anther is mature, it opens and sheds its pollen grains. Pollen grains which land on a receptive stigma soon germinate, each sending out a pollen tube which grows down through the style and into the ovary. The pollen tube first to enter an ovule discharges its male elements which fuse with the female elements of the ovule to form the initial cells that develop into a seed. This fusion of male and female elements constitutes the process of fertilization apply the pollen with the tweezers. The Composites, such as cosmos and zinnias, are particularly difficult to handle in this way because of the very small size of their numerous florets.

MOST FLOWERS SHOULD BE EMASCULATED AND COVERED

An important basic principle is: *When pollen has been received by the stigma, it is too late to bring other pollen to make a cross.* In other words, it is the *first* pollen received which usually results in fertilizing the embryo seeds. For that reason, it is usually wise to remove the anthers from the flower to be pollenized before they shed their pollen and cover this emasculated flower with a paper or cellophane bag a few days before the stigma is ripe. In general, it is wise to avoid substantial mutilation of the petals when removing the anthers, yet in some plants, it does no apparent harm to remove the entire corolla. The source of pollen should likewise be protected with a bag to prevent contamination from foreign pollen carried by insects and wind.

On the other hand, if you are thoroughly familiar with your flowers and are sure you can tell the night before when they will be ready for pollination, you may avoid this work by getting up early in the morning and transferring the pollen before the bees start to visit the blossoms.

It would be wise to examine your flowers frequently in order to determine when the pollen and the stigma will be ready. It would also be wise to make records of your observations; these should be helpful to you in succeeding years. When you have two varieties which you wish to cross and you cannot discover that both are ready for pollination at the same time, it may still be worthwhile to pollinate even though you think the stigma is not quite ready.

As a general rule, a flower sheds its pollen soon after its petals open. There are some, however, which are not quite as prompt as that. It is impossible to give specific information as to the exact time for pollination. This must be discovered by your own study, for not only do plants themselves differ as to time, but the weather and other conditions have a great deal to do with it. It is not difficult to learn the technique of hybridizing plants, but it frequently requires considerable patience.

SOME FLOWERS ARE SELF-FERTILIZED

There are some flowers, of course, which are hermaphrodite. This means that they are self-fertilized. The onion, for example, is hermaphrodite. In order to pollenize an onion successfully, it would be necessary to cut the stamens from the flower which is to receive the pollen and cover it with a bag before the pollen is ready. This will prevent the flower from fertilizing itself. Then, when the pistil is ready, you can carry the pollen from another flower and you should get a successful cross.

HOW TO USE INSECTS FOR POLLINATION

It is possible to use insects for pollination. The way to do that is to plant your varieties close together. The bees and other insects will work on them and will bring about crosses. You will not be sure as to the exact parentage of the crosses; nevertheless, you can get new varieties in this way.

POLLEN MAY BE STORED FOR FUTURE USE

Scientists have learned that they can hold pollen by storing it under proper conditions. They have used it with success several days or weeks later. As a matter of fact, experiments conducted at the University of California have proved that pollen can be stored as long as a year and still be able to fertilize the embryo of the flower. At room temperature, pollen usually remains viable for only a few hours. In a refrigerator, it may be good for as much as two or three weeks. In the California experiments, pollen was placed in a deep freeze in which a temperature of 51 degrees below zero Centigrade was maintained. After 12 months, these samples germinated so perfectly that only 4% was useless.

It would be safe, just for the sake of learning how to do it, to place some pollen in a small glass bottle and store it in an ordinary refrigerator. Undoubtedly, most of it could be kept for several days. This procedure makes it possible to cross two plants even though the pollen is mature on the male parent well in advance of the time when the stigmas of the female parent are receptive.

The conditions which are necessary for successful storage of pollen vary with different species of plants. Pollen of most species, however, requires cool, dry storage for satisfactory longevity.

XVI

The Technique of a Successful Hybridizer

A FRIEND of mine, Mr. Clark A. Pickell of Rochester, New York, has had a lot of fun and some profit from cross-pollenizing gladioli. He has developed a number of new varieties. In a recent letter, he described his work to me as follows :

"My breeding is strictly a hobby, at least fundamentally (I did sell the gladiolus variety Gwen). Most of my work has been with the gladioli with an occasional branching out into other bulbs and the day lilies.

"With the glads, I have in general used two procedures. In the first, I use chance or natural-set seed of selected varieties; and in the second, I use carefully handmade crosses. Actually, both are modified and combined for the end results. For instance, I like to raise a large lot of seedlings from a carefully made cross and then let the best of them set chance seed.

"When I do make crosses, many of them are spur-of-the-moment types made only because two varieties happen to be open at the same time and look as though a combination of the two might produce something interesting. I do have a program of sorts, at least in some of my breeding. From the beginning, I have been interested in the blues and in fragrance. These two characteristics have probably accounted for at least half my crosses to date with fragrance in the lead until recently. To these, I have now added the miniatures.

How to Work for a Single Character

"My procedure, when working for a single character, is to make a number of out crosses [a cross with an unrelated species] with outstanding varieties and then recombine the best of these with each other in the hope that the character I am after will reappear, combined with the

70

best features of the other varieties. For instance, the gladiolus Sulphur Frills has the ideal floret form for a miniature glad as far as I am concerned. It has round, heavily ruffled, heavy textured florets held tight against the stem. However, there are only about half as many florets open at one time as I would like, the stem is too coarse and the color value is about zero. The health is very good.

"I am crossing this with a number of the miniatures, especially those having several florets open at the same time, with outstanding colors in all sizes and with varieties having a large number of open florets regardless of size and color. In the second generation, I will cross these seedlings in a wide variety of combinations, being careful to keep the relationships as far apart as possible with the exception of the Sulphur Frills blood, of course.

"In the third generation, I will become much more critical. I will use only seedlings having six florets open at once and which are well down into the miniature size groups. Color groups will be established and stems will be watched to see that they are not too coarse and that they are long enough. By the fourth generation, if I am lucky, I will have a whole new race of miniature glads with nice round florets, six to eight open on tall slender stems and in a wide range of clear colors.

HYBRIDIZING IS A SIDE LINE

"I have just described an ideal program, of course. My work is electrical engineering and there is not much spare time for my glads so, no doubt, I never will be able to proceed strictly in accordance with it as laid out.

"For a starter, I already have a number of Sulphur Frills seedlings. Last year I grew a number of chance seedlings from one of these out of a cross with Vagabond Prince and got about 25% nice ruffled red and rose seedlings. About a dozen of these have the Sulphur Frills form and size and will be used in future breeding.

"Sulphur Frills crossed with Orange Butterfly (a real small orange which will open eight to ten) gave me a nice group of pale yellow and light pink seedlings. Not many of these have the Sulphur Frills form but they were quite small with good colors and stems.

"From Sulphur Frills crossed onto two whites and then recombined, I have a seedling which has reverted to Sulphur Frills for color and floret form although it opens wider but it will open five to six florets to the usual three on Sulphur Frills and the stem is slim and twice as long.

"One of my older seedlings from Sulphur Frills and a purple seedling is a nice heavily ruffled lavender but the stem is coarse and the flower head clubby.

"This will be added to from time to time and crosses made between them in various combinations. The seedlings from the preliminary crosses at least will be permitted to form chance seed.

CROSSING FOR COLOR

"In my blue crosses, I am mostly making crosses of the best blues onto various whites and then re-combining. Two types of selections are being made in this. The first is for the best colors, of course, and the second for the most robust and healthy plants regardless of color. In the second and third generation, color will become more and more important in the second group as well as the first. I am beginning to cross the blues onto the pale yellows and creams too, especially a very large, heavily ruffled, pale yellow seedling with a tinge of green."

A BREEDING PROGRAM

Mr. Pickell also sent me the following extracts from a talk which he gave before a garden club at one time on the subject of plant breeding:

"There are two main methods of procedure in any breeding program. First comes selection, and this is basic, no matter what other devices are used. This may or may not be combined with inter-breeding or 'hybridizing,' as you may prefer to call it; and occasionally may be aided by sports.

"To conduct a breeding program by selection alone is usually slow and involves the growing of large numbers of plants and selecting out a few which most nearly meet the ideal toward which we are aiming, such as color, size, health, etc. Seed is then saved from these few and planted in quantity and the process repeated. This procedure by itself is of special value in maintaining strains which have already been established rather than in the production of radically different types.

SELECTION ALONE IS SOMETIMES SUFFICIENT

"When I was a boy, my father made quite a business of growing onion seed. When his crop was being graded for sale, he would sort out all the best looking bulbs of a certain size and shape for seed stock. These would be set out in the spring and allowed to produce seed. This is a perfect example of breeding by selection. In this case, my father was primarily interested in maintaining the type and quality of his stock.

"He could just as easily have used the same methods to produce new types by selecting the extreme examples most nearly approaching whatever he had in mind. This is the process by which all of our commercial strains of flower and vegetable seeds are kept to standard or improved. This is the method also that must be used when none of our available breeding stock has a certain desired characteristic and we have to build it from scratch, so to speak, such as the production of the deep red, almost black, day lily from the common roadside type.

HYBRIDIZE FOR RADICALLY NEW TYPES

"If the breeder is after radically new types or combinations of characteristics, then straight selection will probably be too slow and he will want to resort to interbreeding of different strains or species to obtain quicker results. He may cross the largest flower with the best color and hope that the two will combine in the resulting seedlings. This may or may not work, depending on several factors such as the purity of the two strains, the types of inheritance involved and just plain luck. The only essential difference between this procedure and straight selection is the artificial control of pollination. This, of course, is necessary in the use of species, for they will not usually accept pollen from another species if it is available from their own.

WATCH FOR SPORTS OR MUTANTS

"A third factor which may be of importance is the occurrence and recognition of sports. These appear unexpectedly and may vary all the way from a plant entirely different from either parent to such slight differences that only the expert will recognize them. A sport is essentially a new type of plant appearing spontaneously in a lot of normal appearing plants and which cannot be explained by any of the known hereditary factors of its parents. Such a plant would be called a seed sport or mutant.

"Occasionally, what is known as a 'bud sport' may occur where one branch of a plant grows different characters than the balance of the plant. The first nasturtium of the gleam type was a seed sport which some observant person happened to find and propagate. The red California poppy was developed from a sport which was observed to have just one red line in one of its petals.

"Bud sports are a little more mysterious. Many of our climbing roses are said to be bud sports from bush types. Bud sports may not breed true if we try to propagate them from seed, but a true seed sport should.

SPORTS PRODUCED ARTIFICIALLY

"To a certain extent, sports may be produced artificially. If the growing tips of some plants are treated with a solution of *colchicine*, a doubling of the chromosome

VENIDIUM HYBRIDS HAVE DAISY-LIKE FLOWERS FOUR OR FIVE INCHES ACROSS

JAPANESE MAPLE LEAVES TAKE MANY DIFFERENT FORMS

7. VARIATION IN LEAVES

8. GAILLARDIA SUN GOD HAS PURE GOLD BLOSSOMS FOUR INCHES ACROSS

9. IN MAKING CUTTINGS OF WOODY PLANTS FOR REPRODUCING A NEW VARIETY, SHORT SECTIONS WITH TWO OR MORE BUDS ARE CUT TO BE GRAFTED ONTO SEEDLING ROOT STOCKS

10. BUNDLES OF CIONS ARE TAKEN TO GRAFTING TABLE. EACH ONE IS GRAFTED ONTO A ROOT STOCK AND SET OUT IN NURSERY FOR DEVELOPMENT BEFORE NEW TREES ARE SOLD TO CUSTOMERS

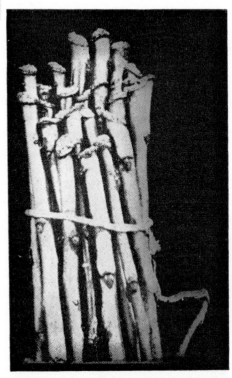

IT IS NOT A DIFFICULT TASK TO LOCATE THE ANTHERS IN MOST KINDS OF FLOWERS BECAUSE OF THEIR USUAL YELLOWISH COLOR, SACKLIKE SHAPE, AND PRESENCE OF NUMEROUS POLLEN GRAINS WHEN MATURE. HOWEVER, THE STIGMA MAY APPEAR QUITE DIFFERENT IN DIFFERENT SPECIES. THE FOUR SPECIES PICTURED OPPOSITE ARE AMONG THOSE WHICH ARE SUFFI-CIENTLY DIFFERENT TO RECEIVE ATTENTION HERE. THE STIGMA OF THE POPPY USUALLY HAS SEVERAL BRANCHES WHICH LIE DIRECTLY ON TOP OF THE OVARY WITHOUT A CONNECTING STYLE, WHEREAS THAT OF THE IRIS IS THE UPPER SURFACE OF THE STRUCTURE IMMEDIATELY ABOVE THE ANTHERS. IN THE CASE OF THE SWEET PEA THE SEX ORGANS WILL BE FOUND INSIDE OF THE KEEL, WITH ALL ANTHERS BEING ATTACHED TO A SHEATH WHICH SURROUNDS THE OVARY. CHRYSANTHEMUMS AND MANY OF THE COMPOSITES HAVE TWO TYPES OF FLORETS IN ONE FLOWER HEAD. THE FORKED STIGMA OF THE RAY FLORET WILL BE FOUND AT THE BASE OF A PETAL, NO ANTHERS BEING PRES-ENT. THE DISK FLORETS WHICH MAKE UP THE CENTER OF THE HEAD ARE ALL PERFECT HAVING BOTH SEXES PRESENT. THE FORKED STIGMA IS PUSHED UP ABOVE THE ANTHERS AND THEN SPREADS ITS BRANCHES AFTER THE POLLEN HAS BEEN SHED IN THAT FLORET

11. LOCATION OF TYPICAL FLOWER ANTHERS
SEE OPPOSITE PAGE FOR FULL DETAILS

IRIS   CHRYSANTHEMUM
SWEET PEA   POPPY

12. TOP—A CORM OF THE GLADIOLUS PRISCILLA ALDEN WITH ITS INCREASE OF THREE CORMLETS.

BOTTOM—THE VARIETY MRS. DR. NORTON WITH AN INCREASE OF HUNDREDS OF CORMLETS

SEE CHAPTER XV

MAY TARRANT   CELESTE

13. MAY TARRANT, A DEEP ROSE HYBRID GLADIOLUS, ALMOST CHERRY RED WITH CREAMY WHITE THROAT, GROWS OVER $4\frac{1}{2}$ FEET TALL. PARENTS ARE MYRNA AND GLAMIS. INTRODUCED BY CHAMPLAIN VIEW GARDENS, IT HAS WON MANY FIRST PRIZES.

14. AN EARLY WHITE GLADIOLUS NAMED CELESTE, ORIGINATED BY PAUL SAVELIEF. THE BLOOMS ARE PURE WHITE AND HEAVILY RUFFLED

EVENING STAR   STATELINESS

15. NEW GLADIOLUS VARIETY SHOWING EXTREME RUFFLING. NAMED EVENING STAR AND INTRODUCED BY CHAMPLAIN VIEW GARDENS, BURLINGTON, VERMONT. THIS IS THE RESULT OF PLANTING A SEED. EACH SEEDLING GLADIOLUS IS A NEW VARIETY, BUT MOST ARE NOT AS GOOD AS PARENT BLOSSOM. THIS IS A REAL SENSATION.

16. STATELINESS IS THE APPROPRIATE NAME FOR THIS BEAUTIFUL GLADIOLUS. IT IS DEEP PINK WITH SOMEWHAT DARKER FEATHER. CHAMPLAIN VIEW GARDENS CATALOGUE SAYS THAT IT OPENS 10 OR 12 BLOSSOMS ON A LONG HEAD

count of that portion of the plant may result. If seeds are then raised from that part of the plant, some very unexpected results may occur.

"Plants or seeds may also be treated with X-rays with unpredictable results in succeeding generations. Even disease may cause sports. The most common example is the rectified or broken tulips, which get their weird streaks and blotches of color from a virus disease. There is a strong suspicion that at least a portion of the sports appearing among gladioli, especially in the variety Picardy, may be of this nature.

"To understand what may result when two varieties or species are crossed, we should know something about their ancestry. Most of our present horticultural varieties of bulbs and other types of plants which are commonly propagated by division are of such mixed ancestry that we can tell very little about what may be expected when they are used as parents, except in a general way, unless we have already used them several times in various crosses. Named strains of plants which are usually grown from seeds, on the other hand, have usually been selected for type, color, etc., for so many generations that the characters have become fixed and these plants will act more or less like species when crossed with other strains.

"Even when we know the various characteristics of the material with which we plan to work, we also need to know how they are inherited if we wish to have some idea ahead of time as to what we are going to produce.

"Most of us have heard the expression: 'Like begets like.' That is true in most plant breeding, at least in a general way. If two red flowers are crossed, we can expect to get mostly red offspring. Perhaps some of them will be darker than either parent and some lighter, but mostly, they will be in between. Some of them may be marked and some clear colors, but don't be too surprised if some of them are white or some other color.

"Sometimes, we find that our breeding material is

sterile—either entirely so or to its own pollen or to foreign pollen. Horse radish has never been known to set seed although it blooms freely. Many lilies are sterile to their own pollen but will set seed to pollen from other lilies.

"Several of the day lilies will not set seed at all but their pollen can sometimes be used on other varieties. Some of the glad species will not hybridize with certain others although they will set seed freely to their own pollen or that of a few other species. Among the cultivated varieties, old Blue Triumphator would not set seed at all and I never heard of but one person who claimed to have obtained pollen enough to make a cross onto some other variety. The relatively new variety Big Top is almost completely sterile although I did manage to get about thirty seeds from it last year from about twenty bulbs by using repeated applications of mixed pollen.

HYBRIDS ARE OFTEN VIGOROUS GROWERS

"So far, we have considered hybridizing or crossbreeding only as a means of combining two or more desirable characters in one plant or strain. There are other benefits to be expected, however. For instance, when two species or strains carefully selected for type for several generations are combined, there is a decided tendency to produce more robust and healthy offspring.

"One example that most of us know about is our so-called hybrid corns and other vegetables. These are usually larger and more productive than either parent. Since the parent strains have been carefully selected for type for many generations they will act much like species when crossed and all the plants in the first generation will be the same since they will all have the same combination of factors for each characteristic.

"We, therefore, get a uniform crop the first year, but if we try to grow seed from this crop, we would get every combination in the book. This increase in size and productiveness is known as 'hybrid vigor' and is probably partially responsible for the greater size and productiveness of our cultivated varieties as compared to the original species from which they have been developed. This may explain why some strains of plants gradually 'run out' after several generations *when new blood is not brought into the strain.*

SELECTION FOLLOWS CROSSING

"Another result from cross-breeding is an increase in the tendency to vary. All cultivated strains and even species tend to vary somewhat from the norm when grown from seeds. It is this tendency to vary that makes it possible to produce new varieties by selection alone. This tendency is much increased in hybrids or crosses between highly inbred strains, even though they may be quite similar in general appearance. This characteristic sometimes makes it desirable to intercross as many *different strains as possible in as many combinations as possible* for two or three generations before starting a selection program, even though they may be quite similar to start with.

"Crosses between closely related individuals on the other hand tend to have the opposite effect. Instead of invigorating the seedlings, it tends to weaken them and, instead of increasing the variety, it tends to fix the various characteristics present. The reasons for this are very easy to understand if you think about them a bit.

"The interbreeding of close relatives increases very markedly the chances that similar factors will unite to make up the pairs for the various characteristics. Thus, all the desirable characters which may be latent in the strain have a good chance to become evident. This usually results in rapid deterioration and dying out of the strain.

"If the original stock is especially healthy and robust, this need not be so, however. The tendency to health can be strengthened by inbreeding if coupled with careful and very rigid selection the same as any other characteristic.

At best, however, there is likely to be some reduction in size and robustness which characterizes hybrids.

SELF-FERTILIZED VARIETIES ARE OFTEN DISAPPOINTING

"Selfed (self-fertilized) seed is of course the most closely inbred of all and will show the effects faster. In the one or two instances where I have tried it in my glad work I have been very disappointed. For some years, I have been interested in fragrant glads and have tried about everything to produce fragrant seedlings. Several years ago I selfed the variety Mibloom which was the first I had discovered of summer flowering glads with fragrance. The seed grew OK but every seedling died the next year before flowering. I planted them in a bad spot, but nothing else planted there died completely.

"Later, I selfed one of my own fragrant seedlings with nearly the same results. Some of these bloomed but many died. Those that did bloom were mostly small and none of them were particularly fragrant. Lately, I have had an itch to self the variety Picardy in quantity and continue to do so for several generations, selecting the most healthy and varied types and colors just to see what can be done with only one source of material to start from.

"In any program of this type, *health* must be the prime consideration, as indeed it should be in any breeding program. This, I am afraid, is the one factor that most amateur breeders pass up, at least in their first efforts. *A big beautiful flower can blind one to a lot of weakness in health and propagating ability.*

"In making a cross, we should remember that Nature does not like selfed seed as a rule, and has taken many means to prevent this happening. In many flowers, the pollen is ripe and gone before the pistil in the same flower is in proper condition to receive it. In others, the pollen is in one flower and the pistil in another, either on the same plant or on another plant. In rather rare cases, flowers are arranged for self-pollination. This is usual in the legumes.

WHEN TO POLLINIZE

"In order to make successful crosses, one must learn to know when both the pollen and the pistil are in the proper condition. The pollen is usually ready as soon as it is dry, which will probably be shortly after the flower opens. There are different ways in which the pistil may show that it is ready. If it is branched, the parts will separate and spread out, usually the sensitive surface will become feathery. In the case of many of the lilies, a drop of sticky liquid will form on the surface. It may be several days after the flower opens when this takes place. In the glads, it is usually the morning of the third day, although crosses may sometimes be effected late on the second day.

WHAT TO EXPECT FROM CROSSING GLADIOLI

"The gladiolus probably has as mixed an ancestry as any flower under cultivation, which makes it difficult to establish any rules as to what may be expected when two varieties are crossed. Very few breeders have made any effort to purify their strains, especially in this country. Some of the European breeders have made some effort to establish pure color strains. In Scotland, the effort has been for formality and many open florets, while in Australia, it has been for huge size.

"In general, I believe that red tends to be dominant over white, although I have seen reds or reddish purples from crosses between two whites. Yellow may be dominant but I think there is more tendency to blend.

"Blues definitely tend to blend and when a blue is crossed onto a white, most of the seedlings will be muddy bluish lavenders or mauves. If these are crossed among themselves, most of the second generation seedlings will be like those in the first generation. Only rarely will one of them even approach the depth of color and clarity of the original blue parent.

"When different colors are crossed, it is hard to form even a good guess as to what may happen. Size may be recessive. I have noticed that when two Picardy seedlings are crossed, an appreciable number of very large offspring may result even though the two parents may not be above average for size.

EXPERIENCES IN BREEDING FOR FRAGRANCE

"Fragrance, as far as the glads are concerned, is a law unto itself. I have worked for this characteristic and, so far, none of the common laws seem to apply. I have found fragrant seedlings in crosses between non-fragrant seedlings. In crosses where both parents are fragrant, only an occasional fragrant seedling may result.

"Sometimes, a cross between a fragrant and a non-fragrant variety will give more fragrant seedlings than when both parents are fragrant. There is a tendency, of course, for the percentage of fragrant seedlings and the strength of the odor to increase as you raise successive generations of crosses between fragrant parents. In the past, there has seemed to be a definite connection between fragrance and small size.

"Some little time ago, I got a very fortunate break when I found a fragrant seedling in a non-fragrant cross which seems entirely free of this link. Last year, an offspring of this seedling and another fragrant seedling was quite fragrant and will place in the largest size group.

"You will occasionally find sterile glads. Just why this should be so is a mystery. This condition usually results from a cross between two parents so distantly related that it is just possible to make the cross. It is almost sure to result in crosses between two generations such as would be the case if a glad were crossed onto a friesia or an iris. In this case, they are called 'mules' and they take their name from the animal of that name which is a cross of the horse and the ass.

GLADIOLI ARE EASY TO BREED

"The gladiolus, because of its size and the accessibility of its sexual parts is very easy to work with. The seeds grow readily and successive generations can be raised every two or three years. An extended breeding program can, therefore, be carried out in a reasonable time. Possibly this is the reason why so many amateur breeders have been working with this flower.

DAY LILIES OFFER POSSIBILITIES

"Another flower that has captured the fancy of amateurs is the day lily. Here, the conditions are entirely different from those in the glads. The variables between different varieties are mostly in size and blooming time. Color variations in the original species and in most of the cultivated varieties are very limited, being mostly in the yellows and oranges. I believe the common roadside lily is the only source of red. With this flower, the problem of sterile varieties is acute.

"The roadside lily, or to give it its specie name, hemerocallis fulva, has never been known to set seed, and the same is true of many varieties. One of the sub-species of fulvae called fulva maculata will produce some seed. Fulva pollen used on other species or varieties will occasionally set some seed, and it is from these hybrids crossed among themselves and the darkest plants selected out and recrossed for several generations that the present highly prized dark reds have come. Even these are mostly muddy or fulvus colors and the bright spectrum reds that we find in the glads.

"Possible goals in work with this flower are pure whites, bright reds or various shades of yellow or orange with pleasing markings of red. My special choice here will be the pure white. Many day lilies are subject to fading in bright sunlight, sometimes turning pure white wherever the sun hits the petals. That is, of course, a very undesirable characteristic in most varieties. I have a theory, however, that if the worst of these are bred together for several generations, the tendency can be so intensified that a pure white seed sport may result. A pure white would not only be very valuable in itself, but should also be very valuable to the breeder for use in the production of new and clearer shades of red, pink, and buff.

OPPORTUNITIES WITH AFRICAN VIOLETS

"Another flower that has captured the imagination of amateur breeders is the African Violet, or Saintpaulia. I will have to confess that I have been bitten also and have several crosses under way. So far, my breeding stock is limited to a white, a pink, a dark blue, and a violet. I have a so-called 'red' on order which will complete the color range so far as I know. I haven't grown any seed yet so do not know what to expect from the seedlings. I have been very much surprised at the length of time required for the seed to mature.

LILIES ARE ENTICING

"Lilies offer the breeder his greatest opportunity and his greatest challenge. Probably in no other family of cultivated plants are the species so generally grown unless it is the orchid.

"Many lilies are subject to several fatal diseases such as mosaic or basal rot. Many beautiful hybrids are lost from these causes before they can be propagated for distribution. Several lilies inherit only from the seed parent. The popular Regal, it is said, can be fertilized with pollen from most any other lily and will seed readily, but all the bulbs grown from it will still be Regals even though you keep trying for several generations.

"There is always the chance that you might get a break, however, if the cross is repeated often enough—or perhaps the reverse cross will work. The opportunities for varied combinations are almost infinite. There are all the colors except blue and there is hint enough of that in Martagon and one or two others to make it tantalizing.

"Other members of the family besides the true lilies have plenty of blue such as in the Hyacinths or the Alliums.   There are all sizes of plants from just a few inches to giants ten to twelve feet high.   There are up-facing types, out-facing and drooping.   There are wide-flaring flowers, long slender trumpets and bells.   Some have the petals rolled back onto themselves.   Some have clear colors; many are spotted; and others have a ray of contrasting color through the center of the petals. Some bloom almost as soon as the snow is gone; others scarcely before it flies again.   There are flowers from an inch across to huge things a foot or more in diameter."

NEW VARIETIES ARE IN DEMAND

An encouraging letter from Alfred L. Moses, a nurseryman who specializes in perennials including iris, roses, gladioli, shrubs, and trees, reads as follows:

"Some seedlings are sold outright for from $50 to $3,500 for the entire stock or for 95% of the entire stock. Others are sold on a percentage, sometimes on a limited sale, through only one seedsman or through a group for a period of years.   The stock in this latter case remains in the hands of the originator. These percentages vary from 25% to 60% based on the retail price.

"We ask that any variety we are requested to introduce should be grown in our test plot at least one year, and preferably two, before we offer it for sale.   This is not always done but it helps us properly to evaluate it. Other than that, we have no rules."

It pays to develop new varieties.   There is both pleasure and profit to be anticipated.

XVII

New Varieties Sometimes Appear from a Single Bud

IN THE September 14, 1947, issue of the *St. Louis Post Dispatch* there were printed color photographs of a beautiful new variety of peach with the following information:

"Something unexplained happened to a peach tree in an Arkansas orchard. One limb bore fruit three weeks ahead of time. That caprice of Nature has resulted in a new variety of peach. It is a yellow freestone which ripens 20 days earlier than Burbank July Elbertas, 40 days earlier than standard Elbertas. Young trees of the new variety will be sold to commercial and home orchardists next year; their fruit will probably be on the market in three years.

"The sport — as such mutations in Nature are known — originated in the orchard of H. Frank Smith at Dover, Arkansas. In June, 1944, he noticed that fruit on one limb of a Burbank July Elberta was already ripe, with other fruit on the same tree still unmatured. He sent cions (fresh shoot cuttings) from the limb to Stark Brothers' nurseries at Louisiana, Missouri. The nurseries, always on the lookout for new varieties of fruit, propagated the cions by budding. In 1946, the budded stock bore nearly three weeks early thus proving constant to the parent limb. Now, buds from the sport are being budded onto seedling root stock to produce orchard trees.

$10,000 PAID FOR A NEW PEACH

"The parent tree is still in Smith's orchard. But it belongs to the Stark Nurseries, which paid Smith $10,000 for sole rights to propagate the sport. The tree is inclosed in a cage to keep buds from being stolen. At the nurseries are about 2,000 of the limb's offspring — budded "Starking Delicious" peach trees. Next year, budded stock of the new variety is expected to total 25,000 trees."

You May Find a $10,000 New Variety
on any Orchard Tree

This is a splendid illustration of what we commonly refer to as a "sport." The technical name is "mutant." For some unexplained reason, Nature occasionally causes a single bud to produce something unlike the rest of the plant. Several of our new varieties of fruits have developed from bud sports. For example, there are several red strains of the Delicious, Winesap, Rome Beauty, McIntosh, and Gravenstein apple varieties.

Bud sports are fairly common on many kinds of vegetatively propagated plants including roses, chrysanthemums, fruits, ornamental shrubs and trees. An interesting case is the nectarine which many people think is a cross between the peach and plum. Actually it has been known to occur as a bud sport on a peach tree from which its fruit differs in but one character, that of having no fuzz on the fruit. In all other characters of the fruit and tree the nectarine is indistinguishable from the peach.

The only way to discover a mutant is to keep your eyes open. The chances are, if you find a valuable mutant, it will stand out from all the other fruits on the tree so that you will not be very likely to miss it, although we do know that many valuable new varieties have been overlooked and lost because the persons who first saw them did not realize their importance.

A friend of mine, O. D. Frank, picked oranges in a neighbor's grove in Florida one day without the thought of discovering a new variety. That evening, when he opened one of the oranges, he noted that it contained no seeds. There were no varieties of seedless orange in the grove from which his basket of oranges had been gathered. It is quite likely that a branch on some tree in that grove was producing seedless fruit, which might have been the beginning of a new seedless variety.

The trouble was, he had no idea as to which tree bore the seedless fruit. Furthermore, if it was a bud sport not all the oranges on that tree were likely to be seedless—probably only those on one branch. The only thing he could do to discover the mutant was to pick from the various trees and cut open the fruit as soon as he picked it in order to find the mutant branch. Obviously, this task of discovering the branch on which a seedless mutant orange is borne is not easy. When the new characteristics are all on the outside where you can observe them as the fruits hang on the trees, it is not so difficult.

WHAT TO DO WHEN YOU FIND A MUTANT

The fact that the one branch of a peach tree in the orchard of Frank Smith of Dover, Arkansas, was worth $10,000 emphasizes the importance of watching for new varieties on the branches of fruit trees. It is necessary to be alert to the value of such changes and it is important to know what to do when you find such a bud sport.

The first thing to do is to study it carefully. Watch the fruit as it develops. Make records as to the exact time of ripening, the size, the color, and so on. Give special note to the branch on which the new fruit is borne, to determine whether or not it has some undesirable characteristic.

In order to sell it, it is important to make a complete record of all of its desirable characteristics, together with any that are undesirable, and then to send samples of the fruit to some dealer who you think might like to introduce it. In the meantime, the branch on which the new fruit is borne should be carefully marked.

One way to mark it would be to attach a shipping label loosely to the branch at the point where it bore fruit different from the rest of the tree. On this label, you could enter certain facts about the new fruit, such as the day discovered, date of its ripening, and so on. In order to protect this label from the weather, it would be wise to enclose it in a cellophane bag.

Another way to mark such a mutant would be to use a piece of white cloth which could be tied securely around the branch and on which there might be a name or number or some other designation to identify the new variety.

The point is, if a nurseryman decides to introduce it as a new variety, he will want to come to your place to see the branch. He will, of course, want to see it at fruiting time, but he might want to visit the tree at other times as well in order to note the blossoming, for example, and the development of the fruit.

How to Propagate a Bud Sport

When you find a new variety which is a mutant of a single bud, you can be quite sure that the seeds borne on the branch will *not* reproduce the variety. It must be reproduced by some *vegetative* method. If it is on a fruit tree, one of the methods of grafting can be used. Small twigs will be taken from the branch and grafted onto root stocks. Perhaps it would be wise to leave this grafting to the nurseryman to whom you sell the new variety. If you wish to do it yourself, it will be necessary, of course, to learn the methods of grafting and you should experiment with some less valuable varieties before attempting to reproduce your mutants.

Several bulletins are listed in Chapter VII of this book in which you will find information about vegetative reproduction. It would be wise to have all of those on hand if you are going to interest yourself in new varieties of several types of plants. If you happen to live near a nursery, it might be easier and better to let one of the expert grafters from the nursery do this work for you.

XVIII

How You Might Introduce Varieties from Other Countries

NOT ALL of the good varieties of plants we are growing commercially in the United States originated here. On the other hand, there are plants which originated here which have been introduced into other countries. The potato and the tomato, for example, both originated in the New World and were later introduced into the Old World.

Our chrysanthemums originated in China. About 500 B. C., Confucius wrote about "The Chrysanthemum In Its Golden Glory." He was a gardener as well as philosopher and grew chrysanthemums in his garden. Early plant explorers took the chrysanthemum to Europe. In 1688, they were grown in Holland, and in 1764 they were grown in England. It is believed that chrysanthemums came to America during Colonial times.

You may be traveling at some time in another country and discover a flower or fruit, either wild or cultivated, which you believe is not grown in the United States. You might be able to bring back seeds, bulbs, or plants and grow them in your own garden as a test. If they prove to be hardy and also seem to have a value, you may then be able to sell the new variety to a seedsman.

Obviously, the most likely place to find varieties which may serve a purpose here is in a climate somewhat similar to our own. It is not very likely that you would find a variety in the tropics which could be introduced into the northern part of the United States. It might be grown in some of the southern states.

You might discover flowers, fruits, or vegetables which would be acceptable in our country. Or it is possible that you might discover an entirely new plant which could be adopted here.

Learn About Plant Quarantines

One caution is necessary: find out about the plant quarantines. There are some plants which our Government would not allow you to import, due to the fact that they are likely to bring in some disease or insect which would be undesirable here. It might be wise, before starting on your trip, to ask the United States Department of Agriculture, Washington, D. C., for information as to quarantines against importing plants from other countries.

Suggestions for testing a new variety have been given in Chapter VII. It is sufficient here to say that you should test a variety brought in from another country under as many different conditions as you can. As suggested in the other chapter, it is also wise to get other people to make tests, preferably experiment stations in different states, in order to get the opinions of others as to the desirability of introducing the plant.

As examples of introductions: the Angouleme pear was introduced from France. It was found there as a wild seedling. It had not been cultivated by orchardists.

The Anjou was also a seedling pear found in France. The Bartlett pear came from Berkshire, England. It was introduced many years ago and, as you know, has been one of our most popular varieties from other countries.

XIX

Be Patient But Persistent

WHILE THERE have been occasions on which a new variety has been found ready for our use, as a general rule, efforts to develop new varieties require a great deal of patience. You may get a thousand new things by planting a thousand seeds, but it is quite likely that all of them will be worthless. On the other hand, you might plant ten seeds and one of them might be worthy of introduction. There is no way to estimate the amount of time it may take to get the plant you desire.

While it requires a tremendous amount of patience, you will find it profitable to be persistent and to keep on trying until you find what you had hoped for.

Continue to plant seeds of those plants which produce a new variety from each seed. Continue to transfer pollen if you are hybridizing. Continue to search the woods and fields and foreign countries for new varieties. Be persistent and you are almost sure to be rewarded.

Many of the new varieties we now enjoy required many years of patient hybridization and selection, but the knowledge that one has made a worthy plant available to mankind is sufficient to justify an entire lifetime of work.

Just think of the thousands — perhaps millions — of people who might benefit from a new fruit, flower, or vegetable which you might have to your credit! When you think of that, you will be encouraged to spend any amount of time to find or develop a new variety which will be worth more to mankind than the varieties now available.

You can be a plant inventor! If you enjoy working with plants, you can have no more important objective.

How Characters Are Inherited

I T IS entirely possible for you, as a practical breeder, to
develop new and better varieties without knowledge of
the process by which characters are transmitted from parent to offspring, or an understanding of the numerous ways
inherited characters may behave in a hybrid from dissimilar
parents. However, after unexpected results have been obtained from some of your crosses, you will wonder why it
turned out "that way."

This brief chapter can but scratch the surface of that
rapidly expanding branch of science, genetics, which con-
cerns itself with the study of heredity in all forms of living
things. Yet it is hoped that the few pages which follow
will add to your appreciation and understanding of whatever plant you may choose for your breeding adventure.

THE BEARERS OF HEREDITY

In an earlier chapter, reference was made to the male
element or nucleus which unites in fertilization with a female nucleus to form the cell from which a new individual
arises. The contents of that cell, with which we are now
concerned, are the chromosomes which most scientists agree
are the structures that transmit most of the characters from
parent to offspring.

Each species of plant has a characteristic number of
these chromosomes. For example, the peach and some species of plum have 16, whereas other plums have 48; the apple 34 or 51; corn 20; tomatoes 24; delphinium 32; and
chrysanthemums may have up to 90. If you are interested
in complete information on this subject it may be found in
the book, "Chromosome Atlas of Cultivated Plants," by
Darlington and Ammal.

The number and structure of these chromosomes has
much to do with the breeding behavior of a plant. If the
variety has an uneven number of chromosomes like the

Gravenstein apple with 51, it usually produces very little, if any, visible pollen and, therefore, may be quite unsatisfactory as a male parent. It is also generally easier to cross two varieties or species which have the same chromosome count. This does not mean that all species with the same number of chromosomes can be readily crossed. The sweet pea, many species of phlox, barley, raspberries and some roses each have 14 chromosomes, yet no two of these can be hybridized. Why? One important reason is that their chromosomes differ greatly in size and structure.

Each normal chromosome has a mate with which it associates under certain conditions. These two chromosomes are spoken of as a "pair" because of their association and the fact that they have to do with the same hereditary units or genes which control the characters of the plant. Dissimilarity normally prevents an association between chromosomes of different pairs even in the same plant. One of the chromosomes in each pair was received from the male parent and the other from the female parent of that individual at the time of fertilization.

THE HEREDITARY UNITS IN SIMPLE CROSSES

Contrasting expressions of most of the characteristics found in plants are said to be controlled or directed by a pair of hereditary units or genes which are located at a certain spot on each member of a pair of chromosomes. The character as it is finally expressed in the plant depends upon the way in which this pair of genes influences each other and are influenced by other genes in that plant.

To illustrate one of the simplest types of behavior: suppose that we crossed a peach and a nectarine. In our hybrid seed, the peach parent has contributed one chromosome carrying a gene for fuzziness of the skin of the fruit while the nectarine parent has contributed a chromosome carrying a gene for no fuzz, or smooth skin, on the fruit. Will the hybrid tree bear peaches, nectarines or something entirely different from either?

In this case, the fuzzy condition of the peach predominates and all of the fruits on the hybrid tree will probably have fuzz like the peach. To all appearances, the fuzzless character of the nectarine has been lost. Yet, if we self-pollinate the blossoms on the hybrid tree and save the resulting seeds, about three-fourths of the trees grown from them will bear fuzzy fruits while one-fourth will bear fuzzless fruits. Thus we see that the fuzzless character, while completely suppressed in the hybrid (F_1) plant, was represented in that plant by a gene because the fuzzless condition reappeared in part of the progeny resulting from self-fertilizing the hybrid.

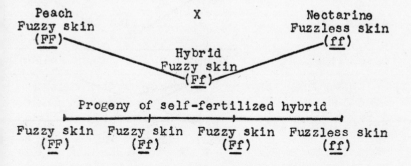

In the above diagram, the letters F and f are used to represent the genes for fuzzy and fuzzless skin respectively. It will be noted that there are two different gene types among the fuzzy skin progeny of the self-fertilized hybrid. Some of them are pure breeding *(FF)* like the peach parent, while others *(Ff)* would behave like the hybrid and produce some fuzzless offspring.

The same type of behavior would be exhibited if we crossed a red-flowered sweet pea and a white one — the hybrid would be red. However, if we had crossed a red snapdragon with a white one, the results would have been somewhat different. In this case, the flowers of the hybrid plant would be pink. The flower color of neither parent dominates that of the other in the color expressed by the hybrid which is different from that found in either parent. This hybrid color is unstable in that it cannot be fixed as would be necessary in a seed-propagated plant before you could offer seed of it for sale as something new. If we self-pollinate this hybrid pink-flowered plant and grow a second generation (F_2) from the resulting seeds, we will find plants of the three flower colors among the progeny.

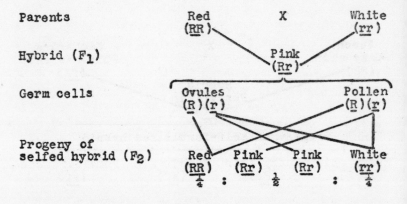

Diagrammatic representation of the inheritance of flower color in the cross between a red and a white flowered Snapdragon plant. This case differs from the previous one only in the fact that the hybrid and half of its progeny express a color which is different from that of either parent.

About one-fourth of these plants will have red flowers and one-fourth white ones like the original parents, whereas about one-half of them will produce pink flowers like the hybrid. Further selfing (self-fertilizing) of these three flower colors will result in the reds and whites breeding true to their respective colors, but the pinks will always produce offspring of the three different flower colors just the same as did the hybrid plant when it was selfed. In other words, it is impossible in this type of case to develop a pure breeding plant with the degree of expression of the character found in the hybrid.

These two different types of character expression in the hybrid are the chief possibilities for many kinds of plant characters. Furthermore, the behavior of flower color or any other character in one kind of plant may be similar to that indicated for the peach-nectarine cross, whereas in a different kind of plant apparently the same character may respond like that of flower color in the snapdragon. Study alone can determine on which basis an unknown character difference in the parents will be expressed in the hybrid. However, both of these examples illustrate one of the basic laws of heredity: *the ability of a character which has been partially or wholly suppressed in a hybrid will reappear in a definite proportion of the progeny which resulted from selfing the hybrid.*

Getting New Combinations of Characters

Let us consider next what happens when the parents differ in two characters and each of these character differences behaves on the same basis as that which we observed in the peach-nectarine cross; i. e., the character found in the hybrid is identical with that found in one of the parents.

Suppose we have two varieties, one with red flowers on a tall plant, the other variety with white flowers on a dwarf plant; and that when we cross these two varieties, the hybrid plants are all like the red-flowered tall parent. Our practical goal, in this case, is to produce a variety which has white flowers on a tall plant. In other words, we desire to combine a character found in one variety with one present in the other parent.

Some people might conclude that, since the hybrid in this case in entirely like one parent, our objective is not possible to obtain. However, if we self-pollinate the hybrid, save the seed, and grow a second generation from it, the following results may be expected: about nine-sixteenths will have red flowers on dwarf plants and three-sixteenths white flowers on tall plants, whereas, one-sixteenth of the plants should produce white flowers and be dwarf in stature like the other parent. Thus, by self-pollinating the hybrid, we have been able to obtain the new combination of characters which we desired. At the same time, we have demonstrated another of the basic laws of heredity: *in many cases, pairs of genes are inherited independently of each other, thus permitting new combinations of characters which they control.*

From a practical breeding standpoint, our job is not finished, if the plant with which we are working must be seed-propagated. About two-thirds of those white talls will be impure for the tall character. Therefore, each plant having this desired combination of characters must undergo one to several generations of selfing coupled with selection for seed stock of only those lines which produce all white flowered tall plants after selfing.

MORE COMPLEX INHERITANCE

Most of the cases in which the plant breeder is interested are not nearly so simple as the examples in the preceding paragraphs. In some cases, you may seek a new combination of several desirable characters. The greater the number of characters involved, the larger must be the number of progeny raised and the less the likelihood of obtaining the desired new combination of characters. Therefore, it is wise to make your breeding objective as simple as possible.

In other cases, notably flower color in all its shades and hues, the character is frequently controlled by two or sev-

Parents   Red Tall   White Dwarf
                     (RRTT)   X   (rrtt)

Hybrid   Red Tall
                           (RrTt)

Germ cells Pollen

	RT	Rt	rT	rt
Ovules RT	Red tall (RRTT)	Red tall (RRTt)	Red tall (RrTT)	Red Tall (RrTt)
Rt	Red tall (RRTt)	Red dwarf (RRtt)	Red tall (RrTt)	Red dwarf (Rrtt)
rT	Red tall (RrTT)	Red tall (RrTt)	White tall (rrTT)	White tall (rrTt)
rt	Red tall (RrTt)	Red dwarf (Rrtt)	White tall (rrTt)	White dwarf (rrtt)

F_2

In the above diagram, the genes found in the hybrid are always *(RrTt)* because the germ cells of each parent carry only one gene of each pair. Thus *R* and *T* were received from one parent while *r* and *t* came from the other parent. The hybrid forms four types of ovules and pollen grains in equal number which combine at random giving the combinations of genes and characters shown in sixteen squares which represent the possibilities to be found among the progeny of the selfed hybrid. When like combinations of characters are added together, it will be found that there are 9 Red tall: 3 Red dwarf: 3 White tall: 1 White dwarf. However, not all of the Red talls, Red dwarfs, or White talls have the same gene types in their makeups.

eral pairs of genes. For example, the difference between white on the one hand and red and blue colors on the other hand is frequently controlled as follows: one pair of genes may control the red-white relationship with the red color completely dominating the expression of white in the hybrid; whereas another pair of genes may cause the red color to turn blue yet have no visible action unless the gene for red color is present. Thus two or more types of white having different breeding behavior are possible.

This situation frequently accounts for those cases where two white flowered plants may be the parents of a hybrid having colored flowers, or where a flower color different from that of either parent, and perhaps entirely new, appears in the hybrid. There are also genes which modify the pattern, intensity, and purity of a flower or fruit color.

Many characters having to do with such things as size, weight and number are controlled by a great many pairs of genes. If you were to cross a large-fruited squash variety with a small-fruited one, it is very probable that the hybrid would bear medium sized squashes but that, among the progeny of the hybrid, some plants would produce large, others medium or small or any other size ranging from at least as large as the larger parent to possibly smaller than the smaller parent. From among these plants, it should be possible by continued selfing and selection to establish a new variety having almost any desired size of squash within reasonable limits. Such characters are much more difficult to fix than color, as a rule, because their expression is strongly influenced by the environment in which the plant is grown.

RESTRICTED RE-COMBINATIONS

The numerous characters of which any plant is composed are collectively controlled by a great many pairs of genes which interact with each other in various ways to produce the end result which you see. Yet all of these genes are thought to be carried on the limited number of pairs of chromosomes found in a cell. A cell of the corn plant, for example, which has but ten pairs of chromosomes, doubtless has several hundred pairs of genes. Each pair of chromosomes must, therefore, carry many pairs of genes.

The genes in one pair of chromosomes behave independently of genes in all other pairs so far as their ability to form new combinations is concerned. However, those genes which are carried on one chromosome are transmitted more or less as a group to one individual in the next generation. Such genes are said to be "linked" because new combinations of the characters controlled by them occur less frequently than would be the case if the genes in question were carried on different pairs of chromosomes. In many cases, such new combinations are not frequently found.

The fact of linkage is of great importance and interest to the geneticist because it makes possible a method by which he can determine the location of each gene on a chromosome. However, it is also of interest to the practical breeder because it frequently helps to account for his inability to obtain seedlings having a new combination of characters which he greatly desires.

For more information along this and related lines of concern to the plant breeder you are referred to the following books:

Crane, M. B., and W. J. C. Lawrence: *The Genetics of Garden Plants;* 3rd Edition. London: Macmillan.

Lawrence, W. J. C.: *Practical Plant Breeding;* 2nd Edition. London: Geo. Allen and Unwin, 1948.

Sinnott, E. W., L. C. Dunn and Dobzansky: *Principles of Genetics;* 4th Edition. New York: McGraw-Hill, 1951.

INDEX